COLLINS COBUILD

COLLINS Birmingham University International Language Database

English Course

Jane & Dave Willis

Practice Book

Collins ELT
8 Grafton Street
London W1X 3LA

COBUILD is a trademark of William Collins Sons & Co. Ltd

10 9 8 7 6 5 4 3 2 1

First published 1989

Printed and bound in Great Britain

ISBN 0 00 370235 9

Design: Caroline Archer
Cover Design: Richard Morris
Artwork: Terry Burton, Dave Eaton, Steve Gibson, Clare
Melinsky, Mike Mosedale

This Practice Book accompanies the Student's Book
ISBN 0 00 370234 0, a set of cassettes ISBN 0 00 370237 5
and a Teacher's Book ISBN 0 00 370236 7

**COBUILD is the Collins Birmingham University International
Language Database**

Acknowledgements

The authors and publishers are grateful to the following for
permission to reproduce material: best (68,91,95,121,220), Cicero
School (135), Robin Corry (198,202), Keiji Fujita, Hadia Malek
El-Ashkar, Billy Gorman, Lura Stoker, Donald M. Phiri for
extracts from Cry for Our Beautiful World, ed. Helen Exley ©
1985 Exley Publications Ltd (223), Loving Magazine, IPC
Magazines (171), The Meteorological Office (210), Midland Bank
plc (25,32), The Observer (182), Pan Books Ltd (55), Penguin
Books Ltd (3), Sealink U.K. Limited (204), Paul Smith for extract
from The Book of Nastier Legends, Routledge and Kegan Paul
(105), Solo Syndication and Literary Agency Ltd (210), Today
(23,34,70,71,143,149,182,246).

The publishers are grateful to the following for the use of
photographs: Nance Fyson (32), Natural History Photographic
Agency (91), Rex Features Ltd (220), Today (34).

Thanks are due to Debbie Powell for helping to provide the wide
variety of interesting authentic texts and to Anthony Forrester,
Georgina Pearce and Paula Walker for their valuable feedback on
the manuscript.

Every effort has been made to contact the owners of copyright
material. In some cases this has not been possible. The publishers
apologise for any omissions, and will be glad to rectify these when
the title is reprinted if details are sent.

Contents

Unit 1
Come stranger, come friend

1 Something in common?

Reasons for learning English

Complete some of these sentences. If you wish, you may use some of the ideas below. You will need to add some words and make some changes.

My main reason for learning English is that my parents thought it would help me find a job and get quicker promotion.

My main reason for learning English is . . .
I also feel that . . .
It would be useful if I could . . .
I'd quite like to be able to . . .
However, I don't really need to be able to . . .

– to be able to talk/write to other business people/ students who don't speak my language/tourists in my country.
– I often/hope to travel overseas/attend international conferences/visit countries where English is understood.
– read English newspapers/stories/letters/text books . . .
– understand what's on the radio/TV news
– watch TV, videos or films in English.
– I need English for my job/to find a good job/to get promotion/for my studies.

3 Writing about a person

A/an or the?

Here is a short biography of George Orwell, one of Britain's best known writers.

a Read it then complete it, putting a/an or the or leaving a blank, as appropriate. The first two are done for you.

> George Orwell (whose real name was Eric Blair) was born in ____ India in 1903, and was educated at Eton. From 1922 to 1928 he served in Burma in **the** Indian Imperial Police. For **the** next two years he lived in Paris, and then came to England as ____ school-teacher. Later he worked in ____ book-shop. In 1937 he went to ____ Spain to fight for ____ Republicans and was wounded. During ____ Second World War he was ____ member of the Home Guard and worked for ____ B.B.C. He died in ____ London in 1950.

b Underline the phrases with the following prepositions, and notice whether they refer to time, place or people.

    at   during   for   from   in   to

c Write six questions that can be answered from the text and one that can't be. If you wish you can begin with:

What/Where was . . . Where did . . . At what point did . . . Who did . . . How long . . . etc.

Who did he fight for in Spain? At what point in his life did he work for the BBC?

4 Family photographs

Read this extract from the recording of Rachel talking about her family photograph.

RS: . . . earlier on. I said I had five sisters, in fact what I meant was, there are five girls in the family.
BB: Ah, I see.
RS: I've got four sisters. In the front here, with the long hair and ear-rings, is Sarah Jane. She's the eldest. On the right here is my sister Emma, and she's the next – just slightly older than me, a couple of years, twenty-nine. And this is me here, with a slightly different hairstyle, and here's my younger brother, although he looks a little older, 'cause he's taller.
BB: Mm. Yes. How tall is he?
RS: I think he's about five-foot-ten . . . inches.
BB: He looks fairly tall.
RS: That's my little half-sister Lucy. She's an absolute sweetie. She's much taller than that now. This was taken a couple of years ago. And this is Kate, who's also – er younger than me. She's nineteen.
BB: I can see the family resemblance all round.
RS: Yes, there is, isn't there? The actual colour, er . . . I'm red-headed, and so's my sister Kate and Sarah-Jane. But I think . . .

a Write the names of her family in order of age.

b Complete this paragraph about Kate.

Kate comes from quite a large family – in fact she has one _____ and four sisters, three _____ _____ and one _____. Kate herself is 19. She has _____ _____ like her sisters Rachel and _____. From the photo, I remember that she looks _____
_____

c Write a short paragraph in a similar style about Sarah-Jane.

4

Comments

a Write some suitable comments using and adapting phrases from this table. Then write some of your own, and be prepared to say when you might use them.

It That	must be is must have been was sounds looks	quite very a bit slightly fairly pretty really _____ _____	interesting, tiring, pleasant, hard work, boring, difficult, exciting, _____ _____	working as a waitress. being retired. doing the gardening. travelling to different places. practising music every day. going into business on your own. _____ _____

b Choose four sentences and rewrite them in a different order, like this:

Practising the piano every day must be pretty boring.

c Read these comments, then think of some more you might say yourself.

What a smashing photo!
They sound such nice people!
That looks like an interesting story!

_____

_____

It was . . . who/that

Some of the statements below are not quite true. Read again the transcripts in section 4 where Rachel talks to Bruce about her family and correct the false sentences by using a sentence beginning with:

It is/was . . . who

It is Rachel who has a slightly different hair style.

a Rachel has four sisters.
b Emma had a slightly different hairstyle from the one she has now.
c Emma is the eldest.
d Bruce said he had five sisters.
e Emma is twenty nine.
f Rachel's brother is a couple of years older than Rachel.
g Rachel asked how tall her brother was.
h Lucy looks fairly tall.
i Kate and Emma are both younger than Rachel.
j Bruce said he could see the family likeness all round.
k Lucy, Kate and Sarah-Jane all have red hair.

Writing notes

Write brief notes for a talk or a short composition of about 90–100 words on <u>one</u> of these topics.

a A place I would really like to go to.
Describe the place – where it is, what it looks like – and say why you'd like to go there.

b My favourite place on earth.
Describe the place and say how you first discovered it. Explain why you like it so much.

What preposition?

Complete these sentences by inserting <u>at</u>, <u>on</u>, <u>into</u>, <u>in</u>, <u>of</u>, or <u>with</u> in the gaps.

a This is about the fourth _____ a series of photos.
b It's one _____ my favourite photos.
c He's _____ University _____ the moment.
d We collapsed _____ a chair _____ a cup _____ tea.
e This is up _____ the North West.
f Barrow, which is _____ the edge _____ the Lake District.

Grammar words

At the back you will find a **Grammar Book**. After each Practice Book unit, you will study one important Grammar Word, with its uses and typical structures.

> **The Grammar Word for this unit is a/an.**
> **See Grammar Book page 52.**

Unit 2 — The Yetties

13 The Yetties

Preposition practice

This is a slightly different version of the reading passage in the Student's Book. Can you spot one additional piece of information? After reading it, find the word that best fits each space.

all over	around	beyond	during	for
from	in	in	in	of	on	since	to	up to

_____ _____ 1965, the Yetties worked _____ the day and gave concerts _____ the evenings _____ the villages _____ Yetminster. But they found they had so many singing engagements that they took a three-month break _____ their day-time jobs and entered the world _____ professional entertaining _____ the first time. _____ then, their career success has taken them _____ Dorset, in fact _____ _____ the United Kingdom and Europe, and more recently _____ the Far East. They have made records, appeared _____ television, taken part _____ several folk music series, and are still doing their own radio shows.

14 Folksinging and other music

Write a short paragraph about your musical tastes. Use some of the ideas here, but change the sentences as necessary, and add anything you wish.

I really like ... best.
I prefer ... to ....
I'm not really very keen on ...
One of my favourite composers/singers/players/pop stars is ....
Most of my records/cassettes are ... but I also ...
I often/sometimes/occasionally go to concerts, especially ...
The best ... I've ever heard was ... when ....
My family ...

15 Language study

Combine words from each set to make a noun phrase.

1	television	a matches
2	folk	b Kingdom
3	football	c music
4	Saturday	d outings
5	coach	e demonstrations
6	political	f series
7	factory	g nights
8	school	h stereos
9	desert	i playgrounds
10	solar-powered	j floors
11	United	k island

17 The Yetties interviewed

Useful phrases from Pete's interview

a   Find the word thing in each quotation. Which of these does it refer to?

an object   an event/events   the show
a problem/problems   the Scouts
other times   an occasion   life in general
similar types of work

b   What is 'd short for? (There are four in quotations 1 and 2).

c   Circle four phrases that are typical of spoken rather than written language.

PETE
1 I'd been to see a show they'd put on ... I thought this was great. It seemed like a pretty good thing.
2 I'd met Mac at School ... and he was in the Scouts, you see, and so I thought, well, this'd be a good thing to join.
3 Originally it was the Women's Institute ... eventually ... the older ones got fed up and they left, and so it really became a thing for young people, you know.

MAC
4 Things were building up; work was getting, you know ... getting in the way of singing.
5 ... very difficult working in a day job and then working evenings, weekends and everything.

19 Grammar

Habitual action – past and present

Use the verbs in brackets to make sentences expressing habitual action. There are two or three different ways of filling each space. You may need to change the form of the verb.

I love camping. We _used to do_ [do] a lot as children. We still _go_ [go] now, in fact, with our children.

In those days we _would_ [take] our bicycles, and by the evening we _____ [be] tired out, so we _____ [sit] round the camp fire and _____ [sing] songs. Now, what we normally do is _____ [travel] by car, and _____ [spend] more time walking.

But our children always _____ [ask] us about what we _____ [do] when we were young, and what we _____ [take] with us. So now in the evenings we often _____ [tell] them stories about the old days – the people we _____ [go] camping with, and the kind of places we _____ [stay] in.

20 Society and song

Vocabulary revision

Match words or phrases with a similar meaning.

drama   farming
from generation to   looking hard
   generation   not often
agricultural   from parents
searching   to children
seldom   theatre, plays
native   to do with
passed on   the countryside
rural   handed on
    where you are born

Try to fill the spaces with a suitable preposition then check by reading the text in your Student's Book, starting from the fourth paragraph.

a   The songs satisfied a need _____ the people who sang them and heard them.

b   They were passed on _____ one _____ another _____ memory, _____ each singer unconsciously developing his own version.

c   The Yetties have been actively involved _____ the revival of folk music _____ folk singers _____ over 15 years.

d   They are still actively involved _____ the life _____ the village, much _____ the manner _____ the village bands of days gone _____ .

Look up any words you still don't know.

23 Review

Reading comprehension

a   **Read this short summary of a news item story. Then read the newspaper story itself. There is one error in the summary. Can you find it?**

A shy young singer with a very fine voice went to a recording studio in Norwich five weeks ago, and made some recordings of songs she had written. She left a tape in the studio which was later heard by some experts in pop music. They realised she was so good she could become a pop-star. So now she is working together with Ross Bradbury, the head of the studio, on a sensational song.

Record bosses hunt a shy star

OPPORTUNITY is knocking for a sensational new girl singer.

But she's so unknown nobody can find out who she is.

The shy blonde left a tape after hiring a recording studio five weeks ago.

Now pop experts who heard it are desperate to trace her and promise: "We can make you a star."

Ross Bradbury, 24, head of RTB recording studios in Norwich said: "She's got a fab-

ulous voice. She reminds me of Karen Carpenter or Suzanne Vega.

Guitar

"She sang a couple of her own compositions which were terrific. I think she's got what it takes."

The slightly-built girl, who was in her early twenties, gave the name Andrea Berdette.

But efforts to trace her through music contacts and newspaper adverts have failed.

b   1   Find three words in the story which mean very very good.

    2   Underline four phrases which describe the singer.

    3   Find the word which means <u>find</u> . Which word in the headline means <u>look for/search for</u> ?

c   **Put a circle round the letter of the phrase which best completes each sentence.**

1   The unknown girl . . .
    a   is a famous new pop singer.
    b   has a fantastic voice and can write her own songs.
    c   has fair hair, is of medium build, and is about 22 or 23.
    d   definitely has the opportunity to become a pop star.

2   After her session in the recording studio five weeks ago . . .
    a   she has been contacted through a newspaper advert.
    b   pop experts are helping to make her a star, as they promised.
    c   Ross Bradbury and the pop experts realised that with her voice, she could become a pop star.
    d   Ross and the pop experts have managed to use their music contacts to trace the unknown girl singer.

d   Quiz

Find the answer from this box for each question.

an instrument	mental	a boss	some drama
a president	rural	wealthy	satisfied
freedom	chap	firmly	

1   If you were in prison, what would you wish for? _____

2   What word describes the countryside as opposed to the town? _____

3   What is a guitar? _____

4   What is an informal word for manager or chief? _____

5   What is an informal word for man? _____

6   What sort of entertainment would you see if you went to the theatre? _____

7   What word means to do with the mind? _____

8   What's another word for rich? _____

9   A kingdom has a king. What does a republic have? _____

10   How would you talk to a small child who was behaving badly? _____

11   If someone had eaten well, and enjoyed their meal, how would you assume they felt? _____

> **The Grammar Word for this unit is it.**
> **See Grammar Book page 57.**

Unit 3
Into business

25 More Golden Rules

Here is another set of 'golden rules' for letters applying for jobs:

> **Remember**
> **Do** include the name of the person you're writing to if you know it.
> **Do** say where you saw their job vacancy advertisement.
> **Do** make sure you have given all the information that is asked for.
> **Do** check that all the spellings and punctuations are correct.
> **Do** include the date and any reference number that is quoted.
> **Do** sign off appropriately. 'Dear Sir/Madam' requires 'Yours faithfully', but if you write 'Dear Mr Bloggs', sign off with 'Yours sincerely'.
> **Do** ensure they know your name. Print or type it in full beneath your signature.

Look at this advertisement and the reply to it. Does the reply obey all the golden rules listed here? How many mistakes can you spot? Write one sentence about each mistake, e.g. *She hasn't given her age.*

> **TRAINEE RECEPTIONIST/TYPIST**
> required by busy advertising agent in city centre. If you have good typing skills and a lively personality we can train you in all other aspects of the job. Write giving age, qualifications and experience to Ian Brown, Personnel Manager, Adnews, 19A, High Street, Newtonmoor, NM4 3DH.

> 21 Seaton Drive
> Newtonmoor NM14 3RD
>
> Dear Sir,
> I am writing in reply to your advertisement last week. I left school last year and since then I have past RSA Typing stage 2.
> I hope I am suitable for your job.
> I look forward to hearing from you.
> Yours faithfully
> Kelly Nicholson

Plan and write this letter out again, according to the golden rules above.

26 Dictionary Skills

a Count or uncount?

The same noun appears in both sentences; in one it is used in a <u>countable</u> way, and in the other, <u>uncountable</u>. Which is which? Write <u>c</u> or <u>u</u> by each sentence.

a There was general agreement that the fire was important. _____
   Agreements on nuclear weapons do not always work. _____
b She is a well known authority on African fish. _____
   He can speak with authority on all kinds of subjects. _____
c He made a lot of money in business. _____
   They set up a small travel business. _____
d He's very friendly. He enjoys company. _____
   He works for a big oil company. _____
e Crime doesn't pay. _____
   It is a crime to waste good food. _____
f How much experience do you have? _____
   The burglary was a frightening experience. _____
g You shouldn't be afraid of failure. _____
   No decision was reached. The meeting was a failure. _____
h She never completely gave up hope. _____
   She started her new job with high hopes. _____
i Japanese industry is making increasing use of robots. _____
   India has one of the largest film industries in the world. _____
j Where is the pain? _____
   The poor creature was in a lot of pain. _____
k We must find a way to improve quality. _____
   What qualities make a good teacher? _____

b Uncount

Complete these sentences using the <u>uncount</u> nouns given below. You may use a dictionary to help you.

1 She is very old and needs ___*help*___ getting upstairs.
2 One women regularly went to a psychiatrist for _____.
3 You must eat to give you _____.
4 There are many good hotels which offer comfortable _____.
5 Unfortunately the government does not have _____ of the country.
6 He has always been interested in _____.
7 Everyone was happy and there was a lot of _____.
8 Nowadays children don't seem to have any _____ for their parents.
9 We would both like to get jobs in _____.
10 _____ should always be well maintained.
11 Did you watch TV last night? There was lots of _____ about the peace talks.

accommodation	advice	control
help	laughter	machinery	management
music	news	respect.	energy.

27 Word forms

The word in capitals at the end of each sentence can be used to form a word that fits in the blank space. Fill in each blank in this way.

a We do occasionally put an *advertisement* in a Folk Music Magazine. ADVERTISE
b When I left school I didn't have the right _____ for university. QUALIFY
c I am particularly interested in hotel _____ MANAGE.
d I have applied for a job as a _____ manager. TRAIN
e Nowadays it is becoming _____ difficult to get a job. INCREASE
f I had a weekend job as a shop _____. ASSIST
g Make sure that your signature is _____. READ
h Be sure to include the _____ number if there is one. REFER
i Which letter do you think is more _____. EFFECT

28 Verbs with prepositions

Complete these sentences by inserting <u>at</u>, <u>into</u>, <u>through</u>, <u>to</u>, <u>to</u>, <u>up</u> or <u>up to</u> in the gaps.

a Pay careful attention _____ dress, appearance, generally speaking, in the interview.
b It'd be very difficult to go _____ your working life living _____ the image you gave _____ your interview.
c Yeah, that amounts _____ the same thing.
d So we could sum _____ a lot of our points as being self-discipline. They all fall _____ the same sort of general category, really.

29 Instructions

Rewriting

Rewrite each of these instructions starting with the words given below it.

a Do not sound overconfident.
   Avoid...
b If you know the name of the person you are writing to you should include it.
   Do...
c Because I am well qualified he said I should write to you.
   In view of...
d She was pushed by her parents to go to university.
   It was her parents...
e You should not apply for a job if you are not suitably qualified.
   Unless...
f The information you give should be relevant to the job.
   Make...
g If you have a telephone number you should include it.
   Include...
h Don't make an employer think you are unlikely to stay long.
   Don't give...
i The Midland Bank produced a magazine which gave ten golden rules.
   A magazine...
j First write a rough draft of your letter.
   Begin...

32 Why go to college?

Read these short paragraphs then complete them with a sentence from below by writing the letter of the best sentence in the gap. The first one has been done for you.

Varied Life – Amanda decided to go to the College of Art and Technology in Newcastle. 'I left school without enough qualifications to go into the job I wanted in art and design. _____ Something I never thought of when I started.'

Meeting People – David is quite clear about why he applied to go the Royal Scottish Academy of Music in Glasgow. You do a lot of playing,' he says. _____ Besides his grant, David expects to get money from playing gigs with bands and teaching. _____ he says, _____

From Science to Politics – Douglas, 19, from Aberdeenshire is reading politics and law at university. _____ 'At school I enjoyed working with computers and was looking forward to the course at university', he said. _____ really like what I'm doing now and it just goes to show. _____

Pushed by Parents – Maggie didn't really want to go to college. 'It was my parents who pushed me. They reckoned if I didn't go then I never would. _____ I'd had too good a time between school and college travelling and working around Europe. _____ I nearly dropped out after my first year, but I'm glad I've stuck it out to my third year.'

a You have to do a lot of practice.
b when you're still at school you don't always know what you will enjoy at university.
c But by the end of the first term I felt completely different.
d He had taken the first year of a computer science course, but was allowed to start again.
e And everyone else in the family had been.
f You make a lot of contacts. It's not a passport to the music profession, but you meet people and your name gets around.
g I didn't imagine life would be so varied, and although I'm still interested in getting a job in display, I may decide to take up fashion design.
h I chose Oxford Poly because it seemed more lively than home in Portsmouth.
i which I enjoy anyway.

> The Grammar Word for this unit is <u>as</u>.
> See Grammar Book page 52.

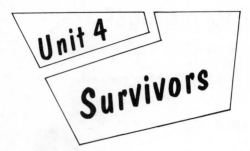

Unit 4
Survivors

34 | Plane panic

Read about John Kelsey-Fry, who is terrified of travelling by plane...

His fear of flying became so severe* that for four years he did not get on a plane.

He is a barrister* and single and the kind of man who might be expected to enjoy holidays all over the world.

"When I was 16, we hit an air pocket as we were coming in to land at Perpignan, in France, and the plane dropped. From then on I got progressively worse.

"You are completely dependent on other people, not just the captain but every technician responsible for maintaining* the plane."

By the time John was 21 his flying phobia* was well established.

After that incident John avoided flying altogether. A year ago, he decided it was ridiculous never to holiday abroad again and he forced himself to fly.

"It is not that I think I am stupid to be frightened. I think everyone else is stupid because they are not."

a Using an arrow, put these sentences into the passage to complete it. The sentences are in the right order, but where do they fit in the passage?

1 "I used to fly a lot as a child and I really enjoyed it," says John.
2 "I have tried to rationalise* it. I think it has something to do with not being in control.
3 "Once I almost could not get on a flight home from New York", he says. "I was in a dreadful state."
4 These days he can just about look out of the plane window but his fear still flies with him.

b The words marked * are explained below. Which word goes with which explanation? Complete the gaps.

_____. a lawyer who speaks in the higher courts of law on behalf of either the defence or the prosecution.

_____. If you _____ something such as a building, road or machine you keep it in good condition by regularly checking it and doing necessary repairs.

_____. terrible fear.

_____. When you _____ something you think of reasons so that you can explain and understand a course of action, belief or state of mind that you are unhappy about.

_____. very bad.

c Now write the questions for which these could be possible answers.

_____?

a For four years.

_____?

b Yes, when he was a child.

_____?

c No, he doesn't, although he obviously has the money to do so.

_____?

d His aeroplane hit an airpocket and dropped.

_____?

e Not only the captain, but every maintenance technician.

_____?

f He got into a dreadful state.

_____?

g He avoided flying altogether.

_____?

h Because he decided it was really silly never to go abroad on holiday.

_____?

i Yes he does now, but he's still afraid.

_____?

j No – he thinks everyone else is stupid not be frightened!

36 | Summary writing

Make all the changes necessary to produce from the following sets of words and phrases sentences which produce a summary of the story of the man who jumped off the Empire State Building.

He said a short prayer and jumped off the...

1 a young artist / decided to kill himself / went to the top of the Empire State Building.
2 a short prayer / jumped.
3 awoke / on a 2 foot ledge / the wind had blown him.
4 knocked on windows / opened by the person inside / couldn't believe what he saw.
5 a happy ending.
6 Hundreds of people called / a guest for Christmas.

Grammar

Verbs with or without objects

One sentence in each pair has a verb without an object. Underline it, and then circle the object in the other sentence.

1 a The fire burned brightly.
1 b We couldn't burn the rubbish because it was raining.
2 a I was only five when the war started.
2 b My father started work when he was ten.
3 a Mr Carter was about to begin his term as president.
3 b It's very difficult. I don't know how to begin.

4 a She stopped and stared at the poster.
4 b You're trying to stop my trip to London.
5 a That doesn't follow.
5 b She promised to follow his advice.
6 a Lynn made for the stairs. Marsha followed.
6 b He's not keen on sport, but he does follow football.
7 a I'll have to move the car.
7 b I was so frightened I couldn't move.
8 a They turned their guns on the crowd.
8 b The key turned easily in the lock.
9 a She idly turned the pages of a magazine.
9 b The wheels started to turn slowly.
10 a Don't strike a match if you smell gas.
10 b There's something in here that smells funny.

Language study

-ing

Complete each of the unfinished sentences so that it means the same as the sentence above it. Where possible, try to use -ing forms.

1 a Some women feel terrified when they go to the supermarket.
1 b For some women ...

going to the supermarket makes them feel terrified.
going to the supermarket is a terrifying experience.

2 a John was so afraid of flying that he could not get on a plane.
2 b John's fear ...
3 a It is your job to keep everything under control.
3 b You are responsible ...

4 a You shouldn't have moved it immediately – you should have called for help.
4 b Instead of ...
5 a We had a breakdown and were about ten minutes late.
5 b As a result ...
6 a He phoned home when he reached his hotel.
6 b On ...
7 a He still couldn't drive even though he took up to ten tranquillisers a day.
7 b In spite of ...
8 a At first I thought that someone was playing a joke on me.
8 b At first I thought it was ...
9 a He had been warned that it was possible that the door would close suddenly.
9 b He had been warned of the possibility ...
10 a He realised that he might die, so he ran on the spot for about ten hours.
10 b Realising ...

Dictionary skills

First read the passage and try to guess the missing words.

Here are some words with their definitions as found in the COBUILD English Dictionary. Say which words go in the blanks.

MILLIONS ARE TOO AFRAID EVEN TO GO OUT SHOPPING

FOR THOUSANDS of women, a trip to the supermarket is one of the most frightening experiences in their lives.

  Their _____ is not simply supermarket stress, when the crowds and the kids and the queues makes shoppers anxious and _____. It is real fear. The urge is to _____ the trolley and run, and some people do.

  The _____, dubbed by experts as Trolley Terror, is a form of _____ dread of open spaces—a condition believed to _____ more than 2 million men and women in Britain.

afflict. If something such as pain or sorrow afflicts someone, it causes them severe physical or mental suffering.
agoraphobia. Is the fear of open spaces or of going outside your home.
dump. If you dump something you throw it away or leave it somewhere because you do not want it any more.
irritable. If you are irritable you are in a mood in which you easily become annoyed.
ordeal. An ordeal is a difficult and extremely unpleasant experience or situation.
syndrome. A medical condition that is characterised by a particular group of signs and symptoms.

The Grammar Word for this unit is in. See Grammar Book page 57.

Unit 5 — Self-expression

43 Henri Matisse

Henri Matisse was one of the world's greatest pioneers in modern art.

Read about Matisse. After the text, you will find a list of answers in note form.

e.g. . . . mother bought him a paint box . . . ill.

Can you write the questions that would give these answers? Then write the answer out in full.

How did Matisse begin painting?
His mother bought him a box of paints when he was ill.

Tahitian Landscape. 1935. Ink.

Henri Emile Benoît Matisse was born in Le Cateau-Cambrésis in northern France on December 31, 1869, the elder of two sons, and grew up in the nearby town of Bohain-en-Vermandois. Intended for the law and eventually his father's grain business, he went to high school in St. Quentin, then to the University in Paris, returning afterwards to St. Quentin to clerk in a law office. Though bored by the law, he felt no particular inclination for anything else. While in Paris, he tells us, he had "had no desire to visit any of the great museums, or even the annual salons of painting."

a   northern France
b   one younger brother
c   father's grain business
d   law
e   not really
f   No interest at all

Then, in his twentieth year, after an attack of appendicitis and during "a fairly long convalescence spent in Bohain, on the advice of a neighbor and following his example, I copied the chromo models [colored reproductions] in a box of paints my mother bought me. My work, already pretty remarkable, must have contained something of my emotion." Matisse had found his calling.

At twenty-two Matisse went back to Paris to study painting. Four years of enlightened academic training brought him the beginnings of conventional success.

g   mother . . . paint box . . . ill
h   twenty
i   a neighbour of his in Bohain
j   twenty-two
k   four years

44 Language study

Examples

a   The words signalling the examples are missing from this text. Choose an appropriate word or phrase from the box. Put it back using an arrow.

for example	for instance	like	such as

Some artists Suzanne Juta start drawing, sketching and painting in early childhood, knowing even from that age that that's what they want to be when they are grown up; others Henri Matisse, one of the pioneers of modern art, come to painting much later in life.

Matisse, famous for paintings Goldfish, only began painting at the age of 20, encouraged by a neighbour of his while he was recovering from an illness.

b   All the punctuation (as well as the words signalling the examples in one of the paragraphs) have been omitted from the rest of this text. Can you put them all back in? (Each paragraph can be one sentence.)

Before that despite the fact that law bored him he had been working as a clerk in a law office intending eventually to go into his fathers grain business

Although Matisse was influenced by artists Gaugin the French Impressionist and Van Gogh well known for his Sunflowers it was Cezanne whose work really inspired him

Ironically it was Van Gogh who said I live in order to paint but who died taking his own life at the age of 37 unable to sell his paintings and make a living out of them

48 Questions you can't ask directly

Make these notes into polite questions and then say what exactly it is you could work out from asking them.

e.g.

what songs were top of the charts when you left school?

(IN ORDER TO WORK OUT THEIR AGE)

a salary/could/architect/first job?
What about/10 years/good firm?

_____

_____

b house prices/your area?/Say for instance/3 bedroom flat/near . . .?

_____

_____

c nice suite/dress!/Where/buy?

_____

d seen/any friends/lately?/What's happened about . . .?

_____

50 *Grammar* ·

Noun plus noun

Write a sentence explaining precisely what is meant by the phrases underlined.

e.g. street art

street art means paintings done on the outside walls of houses or on pavements.

community art . . .
I ended up going to art school . . .
I run music workshops . . .
It's a ten minute journey .
Many children are animal lovers .
A small boy went into a pet shop . . .
He saw the pet shop owner .
There were metal bird cages
and all sorts of food bowls
and water containers . . .

53 Things that children say

Use the pictures to help you work out the last line of this joke.

A small boy went into a pet shop and said to the pet shop owner: "Have you got any dogs going cheap?" "Sorry" the pet shop owner replied," . . .

our   go   'bow wow'   dogs   all

And what about this one?

"Mummy – I got your stamps at the post office. But it was so windy I stuck them on the shopping list . . ."

blow   so   wouldn't   away   they

54 Review

First look at the list of new words in your Student's Book, and check you know their meanings and spellings. Then test your spelling by completing the words in these sentences.

a Being a very cr___t_v_ child she does very __m_g_n_t_v_ drawings, full of c_mpl_x patterns and __xtr___rd_n_r_ shapes.

b He has a very v_s__l mind, a great t__l_nt for drawing, and is hoping to go into __rch_t_ct_r_.

c Buying a house in an __rb_n area is often a good __nv_stm_nt, whereas in a rural area, you can't be so sure.

d In this t_chn_l_g_c_l age, trying to earn a living as an artist is pr_ct_c_ll_ impossible, and many artists get very d_pr_ss_d.

> **The Grammar Word for this unit is the.**
> **See Grammar Book page 59.**

13

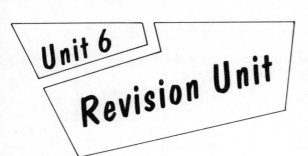

Unit 6 Revision Unit

Writing about people

Here is an extract from the book *The Hitch-hiker's Guide to the Galaxy*. It introduces one of the main characters, Arthur Dent.

> The only person for whom the house was in any way _____ was Arthur Dent, and that was only because it happened to be the one he lived in. He had lived in it for about three years, ever since he had moved out of London because it made him _____ and _____. He was about thirty as well _____, _____ and never quite at ease with himself. The thing that used to worry him most was that people always used to ask him what he was looking so _____ about. He worked in local radio which he always used to tell his friends was a lot more _____ than they probably thought. It was too – most of his friends worked in advertising.

a   Use the words in the box to fill in the blanks:

dark-haired	interesting	irritable
nervous	special	tall	worried

b   **Complete these questions, using information from the text, then answer them.**

1 What was the name of the person for whom . . . ?
2 What was his reason for . . . ?
3 How long . . . ?
4 What kind of a . . . ?
5 What was it that worried . . . ?
6 Where did he and his friends . . . ?
7 Whose . . . ?

Grammar

Wh-words in definitions

A classroom is a room in a school <u>where</u> lessons take place.
A doctor is someone <u>who</u> is qualified in medicine and treats people who <u>are</u> ill.
A nurse is a person <u>whose</u> job is to care for . . .

Can you write definitions for:

a nurse	a hospital	a waiter
a dining room	an architect	a manager
an office	a stranger	a hotel
a policeman	a prison	a criminal

Personality test

a   **Look at these adjectives that can be used to describe people. Divide them into two sets – those that you think are positive and those that you think are negative qualities:**

awkward	beautiful	brilliant
careless	clever	creative
elegant	enthusiastic	friendly
gentle	handsome	happy
healthy	imaginative	independent
keen	kind	neat
practical	reasonable	silly
unpleasant	nasty	decent

b   **Write an appropriate word from above in each space.**

If you are

_____ about something you show a lot of excitement, eagerness or approval.

_____ you have the ability to think up new and original ideas.

_____ you are honest and behave in a way most people approve of.

_____ you are able to make sensible decisions and deal efficiently with problems.

_____ you behave in an unkind or unpleasant way to other people.

_____ you behave in a fair and sensible way.

c   **Write a word you could use to describe someone who:**

. . . makes a lot of silly mistakes. _____

. . . always has a lot of good ideas. _____

. . . always looks very smart. _____

. . . is a very good looking man. _____

. . . is a very good looking woman. _____

. . . is often unkind to other people. _____

d   **Find appropriate words from above for these blanks.**

The most _____/_____est person I know is my brother. He has never failed an exam in his life.

I think my mother is the most _____/_____est person I know. She always enjoys life.

One of the _____est people I know is my uncle. He runs the marathon in under three hours.

e   **Choose five different adjectives from above. Use them to write sentences beginning like this about people you know:**

The kindest/most independent person I know is _____. He/she . . .

14

61 Grammar

Expressing hypotheses

a First try to solve this problem.

A fruit juice seller had two jugs. One jug held three litres and the other held five litres. A customer came up with a very large jug and asked for four litres of fruit juice. How did the seller measure out exactly four litres of juice using only his two jugs?

b List the changes you would need to make to the text above if it started:

A fruit-juice seller has two jugs...

OR

Suppose you were a fruit-juice seller and had only two jugs...

c If you can work out the answer write it out starting:

He takes the five litre jug...

OR

He took the five litre jug...

If you are not sure of the solution to the problem look at the end of this unit before writing your answer.

64 Describing feelings

Here are some words which describe how you feel.

angry	annoyed	bitter	bored
confident	delighted	depressed	sad
exhausted	frightened	guilty	tired
happy	lonely	relaxed	
sorry	terrible	terrific	

a Which five do you like to feel?

b How do you feel when:

... you are at home but all your friends and family are away. _____

... you have nothing to do. _____

... you are very ill. _____

... everything is going wrong. _____

... you have done something wrong. _____

c Choose five other words from above and write sentences starting like this:

I often/always feel _____ when...

66 New words revised

Odd ones out

Circle one or two words or phrases that don't fit in each set.

a benefit   advantage   good result   improvement   depression

b excellent!   oh dear, yes!   Great, yes, indeed!   It's nice   quite strange!   in a sense, quite good.   How difficult!

c allowance   independence   expenses   salary   fees   earnings

d appropriate   excellent   suitable   all right   complaint   relevant   honest   contrast

67 Words in language test instructions

Match instructions that are similar in meaning.

a Describe...
b Explain clearly...
c Summarise briefly
d Find a word that fits suitably in the blank space...
e Complete these sentences by...
f Use this word to form a word that will fit...
g Write an appropriate introduction and conclusion for this...
h Include only information that is relevant.
i Compare and contrast two...

1 Fill the gaps with an appropriate word...
2 Do not add any unnecessary points.
3 Write a short summary of...
4 Write suitable first and last paragraphs for this...
5 Write a comparison for two... showing how they are different.
6 Make another word based on the word given, to go in...
7 Write a full explanation of...
8 Find a word or phrase with which to finish these sentences.
9 Write a description of...

> The Grammar Words for this unit are do/does/did . See Grammar Book page 54.

ANSWER TO THE FRUIT-JUICE SELLER PROBLEM
He took the five litre jug and filled it. He poured three litres into the three litre jug so that he had two litres left in his large jug. He poured this amount into his customer's jug. He repeated this process to make a total of four litres.

Unit 7
Drivers

[68] ## Who make the best drivers?

> A **poll** is a survey in which people are asked their opinion about something.
> A **back seat driver** is a passenger in a car who repeatedly gives advice to the driver without being asked for it.

Family outings usually begin with Dad in the driving seat. But, that's bad news for kids and Dad's aggressive and bad tempered behaviour could be to blame. Gallup quizzed 1,000 children and discovered that while nearly 75% of fathers get cross with other drivers, 53% also shout, 38% swear. However, even when Mum drove the atmosphere didn't get that much lighter – largely, because Dad was even more bad-tempered as a back seat driver.■

These phrases have been missed out of the paragraph above. Put them back using an arrow.

a who find long journeys make them bored, scared or travel sick,
b says a recent survey
c reported the kids

Complete these sentences so they mean the same as the ones in the passage:

d When families go out together, . . .
e Dads are not only bad-tempered when . . .
f The children reported only a slight improvement . . .

16

[70] ## Dictionary skills

Here is some advice about driving on the motorway:

> ● It is courteous to move into middle to allow cars to join the carriageway from slip roads.
> ● Don't dawdle when you are overtaking. Pass through the other car's blind spot as quickly as possible.
> ● When you join the motorway don't be tempted to go straight up to 70 mph. Give yourself time to adjust, especially when roads are congested.
> ● Vary your speed to prevent boredom.

Below are some dictionary definitions. Which words in the passage do they define?

> If you _____ you spend more time than is necessary in doing something or going somewhere.
> If you _____ something you change it so that it is more effective or appropriate.
> _____ is the state of feeling tired because you have lost interest in something or you have nothing to do.
> If you say that you are or feel _____ to do something, you mean that you would like to do it but you feel it would be wrong or inappropriate.
> Someone who is _____ is polite, respectful and considerate.
> A road, area, etc that is _____ is so crowded with traffic or people that normal movement there is impossible.

[71] ## One for the road

Forming words

a The word in capitals at the end of these sentences can be used to form a new word that fits in the blank space. Fill each blank in this way.

1 A lot of accidents are due to _____. CARE
2 There's not a lot of _____ between the way men and women drive. DIFFER
3 Roadworks ahead. Proceed with _____. CAUTIOUS
4 She is a well known _____ of Women's Lib. SUPPORT
5 Once you get nervous your _____ goes. JUDGE
6 It is difficult to make real _____ between the way men drive and the way women drive. COMPARE
7 I didn't know what to do. I felt utterly _____. HELP
8 The first thing to do is _____ the wheel nuts. LOOSE
9 The _____ problem is most serious in the inner cities. RACE
10 I didn't doubt her driving _____. CAPABLE
11 Make sure you _____ the wheel nuts thoroughly. TIGHT

b In Unit 4 you read about people who have strange fears or phobias. Here is another story about someone suffering from a fear of driving.
a Put the parts in the right order.
b Write a two sentence summary of the article.

1 His first panic attack so terrified him that he drove his lorry over pavements to get away.
2 Over the following ten years Tony's agoraphobia was so severe that his wife, Pauline, had to travel with him.
3 TONY BARNARD'S life took a turn for the worse one afternoon in a London traffic jam.
4 His work with Phobic Action means he can drive to work and now once a week he can drive four miles to visit friends.
5 He sought treatment and with Pauline in the passenger seat and up to ten tanquillisers a day, he saved his haulage business.
6 "Last year was so terrible I decided to do something for myself." says Tony. "I am now down to three tranquillisers a day."
(Today Monday March 28 1988)

> **Tranquilliser** a tranquilliser is a drug that makes people calmer and less anxious.
> **Haulage** is the business of transporting goods by road.

72 Any idea how he did it?

Rearrange these phrases to make sentences which retell the story of Claude Padilla from the policeman's point of view.

1 for drunken driving/I stopped a man/and speeding/the other day
2 handcuffed him/of the police car/and put him/I got him out of his car,/in the front passenger seat.
3 then,/start up/while/I heard my car/off the road/I was moving his car
4 and saw him/down the motorway/driving off/in the wrong direction/I looked round
5 chased/after him/I/in his car/and/jumped
6 to about 160 kph/he/kept driving,/he speeded up/not only
7 called/my/for/I/help/for/radio/on
8 was cleared/the motorway/and/was a roadblock/set up

9 thought/that/I/it didn't/would stop him,/but
10 right/it/smashed/he/through
11 we could stop him/eventually/was by putting something/the only way/to puncture his tyres/on the road
12 even then/for another three kilometres/he kept going/finally swerving/before/into a ditch
13 still handcuffed/when/we found/we got to him/he was
14 he/I/how/know/it/did/don't
15 to use his hands/with his knees,/or perhaps/he steered/he sat sideways/maybe/so he was able
16 asked/but/he/him/I/just/laughed
17 did it/how/would love/really/I/to know/he

73 Grammar

It + be + adjective + to

Complete these sentences to make statements that you believe are true:

1 It's polite . . .
2 It's not polite . . .
3 It's easy . . .
4 I think it's silly . . .
5 It's always nice . . .
6 It's a waste of time . . .
7 It's very expensive . . .
8 If you are tired it's . . .
9 If you have plenty of money it's . . .
10 It's unusual . . .

75 Language study

Sentence completion

Rewrite these sentences, starting with the words given, so that they still have a similar meaning.

1 Being cautious is not always a good thing.
    It is not . . .
2 My dad's always putting lots of money into parking meters, but he never wins anything.
    Even though . . .
3 You tend to make a lot of of mistakes when you get nervous.
    Once . . .
4 Show that you intend to pull out.
    Signal your intention . . .
5 Don't move off unless the road is clear.
    If . . .
6 You can see what is behind you without moving your head.
    You don't need . . .
7 It is not always a good thing to drive slowly.
    Driving . . .
8 Look in your mirror to make sure the road is clear.
    Make sure . . .

76 We are all postmen . . .

What single word goes into each of these gaps?
Complete the sentences using the right form of the word:

1 He _____ me a lovely smile.
2 She _____ a very interesting lecture.
3 If you see Andrew could you _____ him a message from me?
4 He _____ a short laugh.
5 My father _____ me all the information I needed.
6 They _____ her the bad news at the hospital.
7 Surely you could have _____ me some warning.
8 Could you _____ me a few examples?
9 He _____ a shout but nobody could hear him.
10 She always _____ very entertaining speeches.
11 He _____ her a lift back to London.
12 They couldn't _____ me any reason for what they had done.

> **The Grammar Word for this unit is have.**
> **See Grammar Book page 55.**

Unit 8
Problems and solutions

Language study ··········

Situation – problem – solution – evaluation

Below are three advertisements. The paragraphs have been mixed up – can you put them in the correct order? It will help if you start by finding the parts of the text which give the problem, the solution and evaluation.

The mini-grill with big ideas

1 Large conventional cookers just don't fit the bill any more when you need fast food or a quick snack. And waiting for the oven to heat up is annoying and needlessly expensive.

2 With today's busy lifestyle our cooking habits have changed.

3 The Teraillon Grille Tout from France is the perfect answer.

Air cooling you can afford

1 There's nothing worse than trying to get your work done – at home or in the office – when the weather gets hot and humid.

2 Now there's an effective alternative.

3 Keep your cool when the weather hots up.

4 The Coolair system will cool you down fast, simply and at a fraction of the cost.

5 But in the past air-conditioning systems have been prohibitively expensive.

Your personal interpreter

1 But now you can forget about having to cart unhelpful phrasebooks around with you – the world's first pocket translator is here.

2 Just enter the word you're looking for and in seconds the translation appears.

3 Though we're travelling abroad more than ever before, most of us are still bad at learning foreign languages.

4 Its micro-electronic circuitry holds more than 8,000 words and has been developed by Langenscheidt, the well know compilers of foreign language dictionaries.

5 Available in three versions – Spanish, French and German – it's small enough to cup in your hand.

6 It translates back into English too.

Language study ··········

Building up complex sentences

Look at how this sentence is gradually built up:

[WHERE?] Water authorities are plagued by seagulls.
Throughout the country water authorities are plagued [WHEN?] by seagulls.
Throughout the country water authorities are plagued, mainly in winter , by [WHAT KIND?] seagulls
Throughout the country water authorities are plagued, mainly in winter, by roosting seagulls [DOING WHAT?]
Throughout the country water authorities are plagued, mainly in winter, by roosting seagulls mucking up their reservoirs .

Now build up sentences from these questions:

1 a [HOW OLD WAS HE?] Peter Emerson was locked in the cold store.
   b [HOW OLD WAS HE?] Peter Emerson was locked in the cold store [WHERE?]
   c [HOW OLD WAS HE?] [WHAT WAS HE?] Peter Emerson was locked in the cold store [WHERE?] [FOR HOW LONG?] [WHAT WAS THE TEMPERATURE?]
   d [HOW OLD WAS HE?] [WHAT WAS HE?] Peter Emerson [WHAT WAS HE DOING YESTERDAY?] after being locked in the cold store [WHERE?] [FOR HOW LONG?] [WHAT WAS THE TEMPERATURE?]
2 a A group of composers and musicologists [FOR EXAMPLE?] felt that the songs would be lost.
   b [WHEN?] a group of musicologists [FOR EXAMPLE?] felt that [WHY WOULD THEY BE LOST?] the [WHAT KIND?] songs [OF WHAT COUNTRY?] would be lost forever [SO WHAT DID THEY DO?]

Grammar ··········

Problems and solutions

Look at this example:

Lots of jobs around the house would be simple enough to do yourself, if only you had the tools the professionals use.

    trouble is
The problem is I don't have the right tools.
    thing is

    answer
The solution is to buy some good tools
    best thing

Make sentences using words like TROUBLE, PROBLEM, ANSWER, SOLUTION and THING based on the following sentences:

a Let this electronic dictionary check your spelling.
b This revolutionary new mobile baby alarm enables you to listen in to your little ones wherever you are in the house – or even the garden.
c Cleaning brass, copper and silver is a dirty task, but these new Magic Gloves provide their own polish and keep hands clean.

What's the problem?

Summary writing

Look at this text and the three summaries, a, b and c, that follow it.

Fizz-Keeper saves that sparkle

How often have you thrown away opened plastic bottles of fizzy drink because they have gone flat? Now with Fizz-Keeper, a simple to use pump that pressurises the airspace left in the bottle, the drink will stay fizzier – and fresher – longer. Tests have shown that bottles fitted with Fizz-Keeper contain up to 60% more carbonation after three days than those with a conventional screw top.

A

Unfortunately fizzy drinks left in plastic bottles often go flat. One solution is to use Fizz-Keeper. This keeps the drink fresher for longer.

B

If fizzy drinks are left in the bottle they are likely to go flat. But Fizz-Keeper helps to keep the drink fresher for longer.

C

Fizzy drinks kept in the bottle are likely to go flat. However, Fizz-Keeper helps to keep drinks fresher for longer.

Now write three similar summaries for this text:

The quick new way to knit

Conventional knitting machines are not only expensive, they're also difficult to use. Not this one. Designed and made in Britain, the Bond Knitting Machine gives the look of hand knitting without all the hard work.

Finally go back to the adverts in section 79 and write a summary for each of those.

88 Review

Fun with words

a Complete these words to make sets of words.

m**o** t**o** r; m**o** t**o** r**i** st; m**o** t**o** rw**a** y.
__nt__nd; __nt__nt__ __n; __nt__nt__ __n__lly.
j__dg__; j__dg__m__nt.
__xp__ct; __xp__ct__d; __n__xp__ct__d;
__n__xp__ct__dly.
c__p__bl__; c__p__bly; c__p__b__l__ty.
__nt__rt__ __n; __nt__rt__ __n__ng;
__nt__rt__ __nm__nt.
s__t__sfy; s__t__sf__ __d; d__ss__t__sf__ __d;
s__t__sf__ct__ __n; d__ss__t__sf__ct__ __n.
__mpr__v__; __mpr__v__d; __mpr__v__ng;
__mpr__v__m__nt.
__bs__rv__; __bs__rv__nt; __bs__rv__t__ __n.

b Rearrange these letters to make sets of words:

mope; tope; topery.

poem; poet; poetry.

esaf; esafun; esafyt.
erfe; erfemod.
ecar; carila; carlialy.
krad; kradsens.
dewi; diwth.
glon; glenth.
gihh; gehith.
borda; beradth.
sybu; sibusens.

c These words are written in phonetic symbols. Rewrite them as ordinary words:

səvaɪv   səvaɪvə   səvaɪvə°l
kɒmplikeit   kɒmplikeɪʃə°n   kɒmplikeɪtɪ²d
kri:eɪt   kri:eɪtiv   kri:eɪʃə°n
dɪ²skraɪb   dɪ²skrɪptiv   dɪ²skrɪpʃə°n
imædʒɪn   imædʒɪnətiv   imædʒɪneɪʃə°n
ɪ²mbærəs   ɪ²mbærəsɪŋ   ɪ²mbærəsmə²nt
ka⁷mbaɪn   ka⁷mbaɪnd   kɒmbɪneɪʃə°n
taɪp   tɪpikə°l   tɪpikə°li⁷
kə⁷mpleɪn   kə⁷mpleɪnd   kə⁷mpleɪnt
kə⁷nteɪn   kə⁷nteɪnd   kə⁷nteɪnz   kɒntɛnt

d Here are four words:

comfort   develop   effect   ordinary

and here are nine parts of words:

-able   dis-   -ed   extra-   -ive
-ly   -ment   un-   under-

Use your dictionary to make as many English words as you can by combining the words with the other parts.

e.g. under   un   ment
able   comfort + able = comfortable   ly
dis   ed   extra   ive

Six words = good,
eight words = very good,
ten words = excellent.

Quiz

1 Which of these can you   a) fold?   b) go for a ride on?
   piece of paper   your arms   a bus   a bicycle   clothes   a horse
2 Which of these is normally hard, or normally soft?
   leather   solid steel   tin   stone   bone
3 what can these be made of?
   a picture frame   a credit card   a wall   a jacket

> The Grammar Word for this unit is of.
> See Grammar Book page 58.

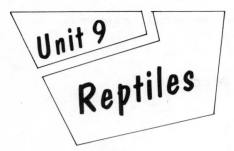

Unit 9 Reptiles

The Chinchilla: a furry friendly creature

Read this passage then fill each blank with one of the words defined on the right.

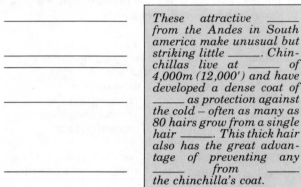

_____

_____

_____

_____

These attractive _____ from the Andes in South america make unusual but striking little _____. Chinchillas live at _____ of 4,000m (12,000') and have developed a dense coat of _____ as protection against the cold – often as many as 80 hairs grow from a single hair _____. This thick hair also has the great advantage of preventing any _____ from _____ the chinchilla's coat.

altitude the altitude of a place is its height above sea level.
follicle a follicle is one of the small hollows in the skin which hairs grow from.
fur is the thick and usually soft hair that grows on the bodies of many mammals.
pet A pet is a tame animal that you keep and look after in your home to give you company and pleasure. Dogs, cats and rabbits are common pets.
parasite a parasite is a small animal or plant that lives in a larger animal or plant and gets its food from it.
penetrate if something penetrates something that is difficult to get through, it succeeds in getting through.
rodent A rodent is a small mammal which has sharp front teeth which are used for gnawing. Rats, mice, rabbits and squirrels are all rodents.

Grammar

a it

Rearrange these words to make sentences.

1 an around interesting it is place to walk
2 difficult finding I it was very
3 does how it learn long take to ?
4 but door good I it kick no open the to tried was
5 and bitterly cold die I I it might realised was
6 a be could for have I it keep me nice picture that to would very
7 a behind car drive hands is it possible tied to with you your ?
8 alligators as have isn't it it's pets they ?
9 a day for good I it me think was
10 it from going handlebars over person stops the the

Now read your sentences and work what the word <u>it</u> refers to in each case.

(See Grammar Book <u>it</u> , page 00.)

b The more ... the more ...

Look at these examples.

The more he saw of the alligators in the zoo the more his fascination grew = <u>As</u> he saw more of the alligators in the zoo <u>so</u> his fascination grew more.

The more blind children handle his snakes the less afraid they will be = <u>If</u> blind children handle his snakes more <u>then</u> they will be less afraid.

The harder you work, the faster you will progress. = <u>If</u> you work harder <u>then</u> you will progress faster.

Rewrite these sentences using patterns like the more ... the more ... or the ——er ... the ——er ...

a <u>As</u> it got colder <u>so</u> he began to walk faster.
   The colder _____ the faster _____
b <u>If</u> you get to know crocodiles more <u>then</u> you will like them more.
   The more _____ the more _____
c <u>As</u> the snake got closer <u>so</u> I became more frightened.
d <u>If</u> you read more <u>then</u> you will learn more.
e <u>As</u> they get older <u>so</u> they become wiser.
f <u>If</u> you earn more <u>then</u> you will spend more.
g <u>As</u> I tried to calm him more <u>so</u> he became angrier.

Read and find the definitions

> Chinchillas were prized for their fur by the local Indians as far back as 1100, but by the 1800s there was also a growing demand from Europe and vast numbers were trapped. As a result, by the early 1900s their continued survival seemed rather doubtful.
>
> Attempts were made in South America to set up a breeding colony, to supply the fur trade but this was unsuccessful at first and it was not really until the 1920s that they started to be bred successfully in captivity in America.

a If you ____ animals or plants you keep them for the purpose of producing more animals or plants.

b ____ is the state of being kept imprisoned or enclosed.

c If there is ____ for something, a lot of the public want to buy it or have it.

d If you ____ something you feel that it is valuable and important, so that you try hard to obtain it.

e ____ is the state of continuing to live in spite of nearly dying or being in great difficulty.

f Someone who ____ animals catches them by using ____.

g If you are ____ in an attempt to do something you do not succeed in doing it.

96 *Language study*

Topic – illustration

Here are a number of sentences which give a general introduction to a topic. Choose five of them and write a sentence to follow it explaining it in more detail:

e.g. Children often say completely unexpected things.

My little sister - aged about three - once looked at an elderly man next to her on the train and asked him why he had such a funny little nose.

a The chinchilla makes an attractive pet.
b Many people believe that all snakes are dangerous, but this is simply not true.
c It is surprising how many people suffer from phobias of different kinds.
d Accidents can happen very easily.
e Men seem to believe that they make better drivers than women.
f It is not easy to become a professional entertainer.
g A lot of people say that your personality depends on your position in the family.

98 *Dictionary skills*

Broad negative adverbs

a Look at the definitions of these adverbs, then read the examples. The adverbs have been taken out of the examples. Mark with an arrow the places in the examples where they should be. The first one is done for you.

> **Barely** you use barely to indicate that the thing you are talking about is only just true or is only just the case. EG *He was so tired that he could stand. This is possible. She looked thirty. The baby was two months old.*
>
> **Hardly 1** Hardly adds a negative quality to what you are saying and so means the thing you are talking about is only just true or not quite true. EG *I was beginning to like Sam, although I knew him. The boy was more than seventeen or eighteen. I could understand a word.*
>
> **2** Hardly is used with words like 'ever', 'any', 'anyone' etc to mean almost, almost never, almost none etc. EG *We ever meet. She had any money. It's worth anything. She had anywhere to go.*
>
> **Scarcely** Scarcely adds a negative quality to what you are saying and so means that the thing you are talking about is only just true or only just the case. EG *I can remember what we ate. They were ever apart. There was a moment they could call their own. It was a very young man who had said this, more than a boy.*

b **Who whose where or which**

Join these sentences with who, whose, where or which to make definitions.

a A zoo is a park. Live animals are kept in a zoo.

A zoo is a park where live animals are kept.

b A trap is a device or hole. It has been placed or dug somewhere in order to catch animals or birds.

c A follicle is a small hollow in the skin. Hairs grow from a follicle.

d A pet is a small animal. You keep a pet in your home.

e A rodent is a small mammal. A rodent has sharp front teeth. It uses these teeth for gnawing.

f A palace is a very large, richly decorated house. A king, queen or president lives in a palace.

g A pop star is a singer. His or her songs are played on popular radio stations.

h A cinema is a building. People go to watch films for entertainment in a cinema.

i The chinchilla is a small animal. Its dense fur is in great demand by the fur trade.

> **The Grammar Word for this unit is the verb to be.**
> **See Grammar Book page 53.**

Wish we hadn't...

101

Language study

Thingummies and thingamabobs

How would you explain these things if you didn't know the words for them?

Choose four things. Write one or two sentences about each one. But first read this explanation. Can you tell which object it is? e.g.

It's a small thing the size of a watch, and you use it to find your direction. It has the words North, South, East and West written on it.

103

Dictionary skills

Definitions with mis-

Look at these definitions and use the words in the box to fill the gaps.

1 If someone, especially a child, _____ they behave in a way which is not acceptable to other people.
2 If you _____ someone or something you form an incorrect idea or opinion about them.
3 If you _____ someone you send them to the wrong place.
4 If you are _____ you are told something that is wrong or inaccurate.
5 If you _____ someone or what they have said or written you give an wrong or inaccurate account of what they have said or written.
6 _____ is the feeling you have relating to someone who you do not trust.
7 To _____ a country means to govern it unfairly or inefficiently.
8 If a plan _____ it goes wrong and does not have the results that you intend it to have.

misjudge	misinformed	mistrust	misfires
misrule	misrepresent	misdirect	misbehaves

105

Grammar

Would have/might have/could have

a   Read the story.

On the carpet

Looking out of the window one morning Mrs Moore saw two men loading her next-door neighbours' expensive Persian carpets into a large van. As her neighbours were away on holiday she was rather worried but instead of calling the police she went outside to confront the pair.

Asking them what they thought they were doing, Mrs Moore was told that they had a contract to collect the carpets and take them for cleaning. Thinking she would take advantage of the situation, she asked if they would also consider including hers. 'Of course,' replied the older of the men, 'it should take about three weeks'.

It was only when the neighbours returned home a week later to find their carpets had been stolen that Mrs Moore realised quite what she had done.

b   **Match each clause from a with a clause from b to make sentences about what happened to Mrs. Moore.**

a   1 If she hadn't looked out of the window ...
   2 She wouldn't have worried ...
   3 She would certainly have called the police ...
   4 If she had called the police ...
   5 If she hadn't believed their story ...
   6 What would you have done ...

b   a ... they could have arrested the men.
   b ... if she had realised they were thieves.
   c ... she might not have seen the two men.
   d ... if her neighbours had been at home.
   e ... if you were Mrs Moore?
   f ... she wouldn't have given them her carpets.

c   **Write a conversation.**

EITHER **Imagine what Mrs Moore said to her husband when he came home from work to find no carpets. What do you think Mr Moore might have said? Write about ten lines of dialogue. For example:**

Mr M: Hello – hey – what's happened to all the carpets?
Mrs M: Well – it was so lucky! You know how badly they needed cleaning? I just happened to look out of the window ...
Mr M: Are you sure ...?

OR **Imagine the conversation that Mrs Moore must have had with her neighbours when they returned from their holiday. Write about ten lines of dialogue. Some ideas are given below.**

Mrs M: Oh, you're back! Did you have a nice time ...
   Neighbours: ...
Mrs M: Well, it's nice to have you back. Oh, by the way, while you were away, ...

106 I wish I hadn't…

Look at this example:

Joe Ramirez should have gone to court by bus.
Joe Ramirez wished *he had gone to court by bus.*

Now complete these sentences in the same way:

1 Mrs Moore should have called the police.
   Mrs Moore wishes…

2 She shouldn't have given the men her carpets.
   She wishes…

3 Mrs Bradbrook should have given clearer
   directions.
   Mrs Bradbrook wished…

4 The gas board official should have listened more
   carefully.
   The gas board official wished…

5 The gas board official should have checked the
   number.
   He wished…

6 Mrs Kerr should have been at home.
   Mrs Kerr wished…

107 *Grammar* ·········

Despite

**Finish each of these sentences so that it means the
same as the complete sentence printed above it.**

1 Mrs Moore did not call the police even though she
   felt very worried.
   In spite of…

2 Although she was suspicious she gave the men her
   own carpets.
   Despite…

3 The Yetties lost their instrument case but they still
   gave their concert.
   In spite of…

4 Even though their case was taken all the way to
   Tokyo it was finally returned to them safely.
   Their case was finally returned safely in spite…

5 Although his case was about to be called Joe
   dashed out to feed the parking meter.
   Despite the fact…

108 Review

a **The word in capitals at the end of each of these
   sentences can be used to form a word that fits
   suitably into the blank space. Fill each blank in
   this way.**

1 The Yetties got to Nepal all right but _____
   their instrument case was lost. FORTUNE

2 The airline apologised to the Yetties for the
   _____ they had caused. CONVENIENT

3 The Yetties accepted their _____.
   APOLOGISE

4 They were a bit _____ about their first Far
   Eastern tour. NERVES

5 They didn't have their own instruments but
   luckily they were able to get _____. PLACE

6 The gas board official _____ Mrs
   Bradbrook's address. HEAR

7 Mrs Kerr made _____ for a neighbour to let
   them in. ARRANGE

8 Mrs Bradbrook finally got the cooker that was
   _____ intended for her. ORIGIN

9 Mrs Kerr was given a _____ cooker.
   CONDITION

10 The cooker was delivered to the wrong
   _____. RESIDENT

11 As far as Mrs Kerr was concerned the cooker was
   quite _____. EXPECT

12 Joe Ramirez had the _____ to be arrested for
   jay walking. FORTUNE

b **Find the odd word out, and explain why.**

a huge   vast   enormous   tiny   massive
b oil   gas   appliance   electricity   coal   solid
   fuel
c depressed   worried   sad   cheerful   unhappy
d despite   in spite of   even though
   meanwhile   although
e judged   granted   gave   presented
f literally   actually   really   unfortunately
   truly
g considerable   appropriate   convenient
   suitable

> **The Grammar Word for this unit is at.**
> **See Grammar Book page 53.**

23

Unit 11 Man-eater

110 The worst possible thing

a Complete this interview by putting the interviewer's questions in.

I: _____

RW: We were on holiday in Tsavo National Park living in one of the bandas there.

I: _____

RW: It's a kind of hut. Usually round with a thatched roof.

I: _____

RW: I heard it first and I woke my wife to let her have a look.

I: _____

RW: No, not at first, we weren't frightened at all.

I: _____

RW: Well we thought it would just go away.

I: _____

RW: I suppose the worst thing was having the baby with us. It wouldn't have been quite so bad if we had been on our own.

I: _____

RW: I don't know. I might have tried to frighten it off with the hurricane lamp. And if things had got really bad I suppose I could have set light to the banda. But I'm, glad it didn't come to that.

I: _____

RW: Oh yes. Twice in fact. And I'd like to go again if I could.

b Complete these sentences:

1 If the baby had been left alone . . .
2 If the leopard had got into the banda . . .
3 . . . he might have set the banda on fire.
4 If his companions hadn't beaten off the leopard . . .

111 *Dictionary skills*

Beat, hit and hold

Match these questions with the answers below:

1 What animal might beat its wings?
2 Who would be likely to beat eggs?
3 When would you be likely to beat time?
4 How could you beat a record?
5 When might you tell someone to beat it?
6 If you made a record and it was a hit would you be pleased?
7 How do you feel if you hit the roof?
8 If an idea hits you does it hurt?
9 When might you be asked to hold the line?
10 If you are held in a cell what are you?

a A cook
b When you wanted them to go away.
c No. You suddenly think of it.
d A bat.
e By running faster than anyone had ever done before.
f Angry.
g A prisoner.
h When listening to music.
i Yes. It would mean it was very popular.
j When making a telephone call.

113 Once a man-eater — always a man-eater

Do you think these statements are true or false?

1 Had the leopard come at night the Webbers would probably have been killed.
2 Had the leopard got into the banda they would probably have escaped.
3 If they hadn't had the baby with them the leopard wouldn't have come.
4 Once a leopard becomes a man-eater the best thing is to shoot it.
5 Had his companions not reacted so quickly the caretaker would certainly have been killed.
6 If they had not kept it away the leopard would have attacked the caretaker again.
7 A stock-killer is even more dangerous than a man-eater.
8 The Webber's leopard behaved very strangely for a man-eater.

 **Grammar** ••••••••••••

Past forms and past participles

a   Say when the underlined words refer to past time.

1 If I <u>saw</u> a man-eater I would be terrified.
2 The man-eater nearly <u>killed</u> the caretaker.
3 Assuming a man-eater <u>attacked</u> you and your family, what would you do?
4 The man-eater <u>was sent</u> to Tsavo by mistake.
5 Suppose one of your friends <u>was attacked</u> by a leopard, what would you do?

b   Divide these words into two groups – good and bad:

pleased   shocked   excited   terrified
worried   delighted   bored   interested
frightened   embarrassed

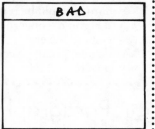

GOOD	BAD

c   Match the first and second parts of these sentences:

1 If I was in hospital with nothing to read and nothing to do . . .
2 If I heard a leopard nearby . . .
3 If I won a lot of money . . .
4 If I broke something valuable belonging to some friends of mine . . .

a   . . . I would be very embarrassed.
b   . . . I would be bored.
c   . . . I would be delighted.
d   . . . I would probably be terrified.

••••••••••••••••••••••••••••••••••

Review

a   A frightening experience with a 'snake'.

Rearrange these phrases to make sentences describing another frightening experience.

1 a very frightening experience/I had/I was living/in West Africa/when
2 I had been told/in that part of the world/that snakes were very common/many of them/and that/were poisonous
3 walking late at night/it was particularly dangerous/without even seeing it/when you could stand on a snake/in fact
4 I was advised/to take a torch* with me/because of this/after dark/whenever I went out
5 one very dark night/to my house/this advice/as I was walking back/I remembered
6 no torch/I had/to see anything/too dark/on the path in front of me/and it was

7 that there were snakes/I began to imagine everywhere/in the shadows/and that I could see them
8 suddenly/on something round/lying/I stood/in the path
9 a rustle* of leaves/there was/on the back of the leg/ and something hit me
10 in the air/and screamed/I jumped/out loud
11 that I had been bitten/I knew/by a poisonous snake

Torch: A torch is a small electric light which you carry in your hand.
Rustle: A rustle is a soft sound made by something moving gently.

Look at the end of this unit to see what happened next.

b   More related words

Can you complete these words?

—pply   —ppl——nc—   —ppl—c—t——n
—ppl—c—nt
b—h—v—   m—sb—h—v—   b—h—v————r
c—nn—ct   d—sc—nn—ct   c—nn—ct——n
c—nstr—ct   c—nstr—ct——n   c—nstr—ct—v—
c—nv—n———nt   —nc—nv—n———t
c—nv—n———c—   —nc—nv—n—c————nc—
f—rt—n—   m—sf—rt—n—   f—rt—n—t—
—nf—rt—n—t—
l—cky   —nl—cky   l—ck—ly   —nl—ck—ly
n—t———n—l—sm   n—t———n—l—st
n—t———n—l—ty
p—rs—n   p—rs—n—l   p—rs—n—lly

Can you pronounce these words? Say them out loud, then spell them in the normal way.

kə'nklu:d   kə'nklu:ʒə°n
i'lɛktrik   ilɛktrɪkə°l   ilektrɪsiti'
feɪvə   feɪvə°rɪt
neɪʃə°n   næʃə°nəl   intənæʃənə°l
rɪ'lʌktənt   rɪlʌktəns
rɛzɪdənt   rɛzɪdəns
θrɛt   θrɛtə°n

c   A frightening experience with a 'snake' Part 2

My leg hurt. Was I going to die? What should I do? Then I remembered I should try to identify the type of snake that had bitten me.

   I peered into the darkness expecting to see a large snake crawling away. Gradually I made out a small branch of a tree. It had a few leaves on and another branch growing out of it. I had stood on the main part of the branch and as it moved, the other part had turned round and hit me sharply on the back of the leg, making a rustling sound as the dry leaves moved. My fear and my imagination had turned a harmless branch into a deadly poisonous snake.

> **The Grammar Word for this unit is get.**
> **See Grammar Book page 55.**

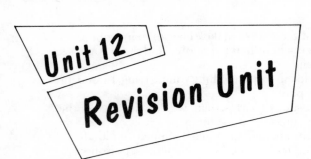

Unit 12 Revision Unit

118 Landscapes and film crews

Sentence completion

Finish the second of each of these pairs of sentences so that it means the same as the first sentence in the pair.

1 A famous film director was planning to film an emotional epilogue to his film.
   There was a famous . . .
2 As they were talking the sun would rise slowly out of the ocean.
   The sun was supposed . . .
3 Often the sunrise is filmed separately and then thrown on a studio screen.
   The usual thing . . .
4 The actors perform in front of this screen and the whole scene is filmed.
   The whole scene is filmed with . . .
5 So the director ordered the camera crew to get a first class sunrise.
   The camera crew . . .
6 But the sun does not rise over the coast of California so they came back empty-handed.
   But because . . .
7 "All right," said the director. "Get me a sunset and we'll run it backwards."
   The director told . . .

b Giving instructions

A.

B.

What instructions might the director have given the actors to tell them to move into their positions in picture B?

e.g. Okay, find your stick and go and stand by . . .
Look as though you're worried that someone might catch you.

Language study

To and that

Rearrange these phrases to make sentences.

1 his original ambition – like his father – an engine driver – was to be
2 often – over the handlebars – that – the problem is – you fly
3 and – I got – in danger – that it was trying – the impression – to get in – we were
4 I thought – interested – the outcome – you would be – to hear – of the leopard incident
5 actually – an accordian – manage to find – we did – we had to mend – that
6 and – get the British Council – we decided – to Nepal – to go on – to sort out the problem
7 a considerate note – however – saying – they were relieved – to find – "Key next door"
8 it had assured – that her cooker – Mrs Kerr – pronto – would be returned
9 and heroine – on a rocky promontory – the hero – to stand – were
10 conclude – I can – very fortunate – only – that you were

121 Paragraph building

More about chinchillas

This continues the article about chinchillas in 91, in Unit 9, but there are some phrases missing. Read it and then rewrite it adding the phrases below in the right places to complete the passage. (The phrases are in the right order to put into the passage.)

In those days a breeding pair could cost £1,800. But prices fell and chinchillas have become a familiar sight. They are nocturnal. Greyish-silver – 'standard' – is the most common colour.

as much as / gradually / since the 1960s / in the home / at their most active in the early morning / although light silver, beige, black and white animals are also available.

Language study

Think of different ways to complete each sentence, using the words given.

a   Walking in the dark in Africa is fine
      as long as ...
      unless ...
      provided that ...
      assuming ...

b   Leopards rarely become man-eaters
      providing ...
      unless ...
      although ...
      despite the fact ...

c   Greyish silver is the most common colour for
    chinchillas,
      though ...
      however ...
      whose ...

d   Chinchillas are nocturnal creatures,
      being ...
      whereas ...
      unlike ...
      which is why ...

123   Summary practice

a   situation – problem – solution – evaluation

Re-read the three parts in Practice Book sections 91, 95 and 121 about chinchillas. Write a summary based on these notes.

Situation:
   Chinchillas,/originally only South America/ beautiful dense fur/due to/extreme cold/height at which they live.

Problem:
   growing demand/fur trade/led to/trapped/and by early 1900s/very few/surviving ./fear/die out .

Solution:
   Attempts made/breed in captivity/breeding colonies/South America.

Evaluation:
   Unsuccessful/until 1920s ./gradually/more success/cheaper/now familiar/pets.

b   hypothesis – evidence – conclusion

Reread the story *On the Carpet* in Practice Book section 105. Answer the questions to make a summary of what happened. Add any words you need.

Hypothesis:
   What did Mrs Moore think when she saw the large van next door?

Evidence (1):
   However, what did the men tell her?

Conclusion (1):
   What conclusion did she draw?
   So what did she ask them to do for her?

Evidence (2):
   What happened when the neighbours returned?

Conclusion (2):
   So what did she realise?

124   A celebration of the seasons

Describing nature

What are the important things about the climate and the countryside in your country, or a country you have seen on TV? Write a few sentences about each of these:

How would you describe the wind for example? Is it soft ... hard ... cruel ... gentle ... fierce ... angry?

What about the sun – is it a friend or an enemy? Does it dry and burn the earth, or gently warm the soil?

What about the rain? Is it welcome or unwelcome? Does it fall gently or beat down, flattening crops and grass?

What colours do you think of in different seasons? Are you surrounded by bright greens and other colours? Or is everything dry and brown? Or various tones of grey?

Which kind of weather makes you feel happiest? saddest? calmest? most lively? Explain why.

128   *Language study*

Questions

a   First read and choose a headline for this story.

A LEARNER driver who had made 13 attempts to pass her test failed again on two counts when she paid a friend to stand in for her. The examiner, alerted by a 27-year difference in their ages, spotted the deception; and the friend, a qualified driver, drove so erratically that she too failed.
   Mr Mark Jones, defending, said of the accused: "She is one of those people who get very, very nervous of tests of any kind. The more times she failed the harder it became for her."

b   Write the questions to which these could be the answers.

a   thirteen.
b   because she kept failing.
c   Yes, he did.
d   the obvious difference in their ages.
e   No, she failed, too.
f   extremely nervous.
g   No. In fact the more times she failed, the harder it became for her.
h   I don't think she ever will.

The Grammar Word for this unit is *if*.
See Grammar Book page 56.

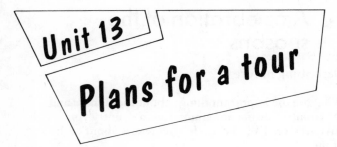

130 Planning the programme

Practice with verbs

Choose the verb you think best fills each space, then change the form of it so that it will fit. You may need to add other words, like to, have, could, may, or will. The first one has been done for you.

decide	make	include	select

1 Once the basic arrangements for a tour _have been made_, the Yetties have to go about _deciding on_ their programme, _____ which songs _____.

play	not visit	grow/become/get	send

2 Normally, if the Yetties _____ these countries before, their records and cassettes _____ to each country in advance, so they can _____ on the local radio stations. Thus the listeners _____ familiar with them.

choose	suit	do	listen	play

3 In order to _____ this, the producer _____ to the songs, then _____ which ones he _____ on the local radio; in other words which ones _____ his listeners' tastes best.

find	give/hand	arrive	plan

4 Then when the Yetties _____ in the country, they are _____ a list of songs that _____ to be the most popular. So they set about _____ a programme around that.

select	be	join	offend	include

5 They try to _____ songs which _____ stories, or choruses, so that the audience _____ in, _____ careful not to choose a song that _____ the audience.

132 Dictionary skills

Practice in using new words

Make correct sentences by putting these words and phrases into the right order.

a   this letter   is   to   attached   of   hotels   a list

b   enclosed   details   of   courses   list   gives   the   available   this year

c   in payment of   I   for £125   my course fees   enclose a cheque

d   bill   be   term   this   this   settled   should   by the end of

e   down   they   quite quickly   after   settled   travelling   all their

f   If   camping   going   too heavy   a   you're   try not to   carry   load

g   The lorry   loaded   had been   unevenly,   was   and   very dangerous   therefore

h   talked   loads   we   about   things   of

i   a valid passport   trip   for this   required   is

j   you   to   required   show   passport   border   stop   and   your   are   at the

k   do not   a child   consider   as important   they

l   the position   have   family   of your   you   considered?

134 Language study

Telexes and letters

Write these telexes out in full, in a style suitable for a business letter. Add any details you feel appropriate.

TIM GITTINGS FROM EDNA LAMBERT. THANKS YOURS 20TH. DELIGHTED ALL OK FOR TRIP. INITIAL FEE PAYMENT £125 REQU'D IMMED'LY. PSE SEND DIRECT TO SCHOOL.

CONGRATS – CONCERT TREMENDOUS SUCCESS. KEEP ALL REVIEWS. PSE TELEX DETAILS YR RETURN TRIP INC ETA. SEE YOU HEATHROW?

REF MEETING BATES & SONS. REGRET NO DEAL DESPITE LOWER PRICES. NOW CONSIDERING NEW FIRM – XML. LIKELY MEETING 22 JUNE. WILL CONTACT U ASAP IF NO GO. GRATEFUL U SEND ADVICE & LATEST REPORT. SORRY.

Letters to a language school

The Cicero School of Languages

42 Upper Grosvenor Road, Tunbridge Wells,
Kent TN1 2ET. Tel: (0892) 47077.
Telex: 94017126 CICE G. Fax: (0892) 22749
Paul Mason BA(Hons)

> Small school in centre of Tunbridge Wells, attractive 17th-century spa town (population 40,000), 60 km south east of London. 15 classrooms, listening centre, video, room-to-room telephone, coffee and games rooms. Teaching in small groups (maximum 10). Tunbridge Wells is surrounded by pretty countryside and interesting places to visit in School's minibus. Golf, swimming, tennis, squash, sailing and riding.

Here is the reply to a letter from Ms Moriaux who runs a training centre (*Service Formation*) in France. She wants to find places in England for a group of students.

a Read the letter and the information about the Cicero School. Then work out what Ms Moriaux must have written in her letter. Write it.

> **11 April 1988**
>
> Ms Dominique Moriaux
> FOL Service Formation
> 17 rue de la Halle au Ble
> 76200
> Dieppe
> France
>
> Dear Ms Moriaux
>
> Thank you for your letter which I received this morning. I have enclosed a brochure which has all the information about our school.
>
> As you will see from our brochure, we do not have students under the age of 16 at the Cicero. However, we work with two associate schools nearby, and we would be delighted to arrange for the younger students to go to one of the associate schools while the rest of the group come to lessons at Cicero.
>
> The younger students would have English lessons in the morning, as do the older students here at Cicero, and would be available for excursions in the afternoons, by arrangement with their principal.
>
> We have been working with both these schools for many years and have placed a large number of students with them, many of whom return year after year.
>
> As I mentioned before, I have enclosed a Cicero brochure, and the brochures for Rock Hill House and Tilsmore Lodge. If you have any further queries, please do not hesitate to contact me again.
>
> Yours sincerely
>
> Anne-Marie Glasheen (Mrs)
> Director of Studies

b Assume the following people want to apply to a Language School. Write a list of the queries they might have. Choose two of the people and write the letter that they might write to the language school. You could begin like this:

> *I am planning to go to the UK this July, and saw details of your school in the Brels - Felco guide, I would like some further details and advice.*

a A family with a very shy girl of 16.
b A married couple who'd like accommodation with the same family.
c An 18-year-old mad on music and concerts.
d A middle-aged man who loves golf and warm weather.
e A father with wife and three children of 5, 9, 14 – for all of whom he wants lessons and separate accommodation.
f A well-off business man who'd like hotel accommodation.

c Write a list of the advantages of staying in an English family rather than in a hotel.

Grammar

Prepositions to end or begin clauses

Choose an appropriate preposition from the box for each space.

from in of through to with

1 One or two of the schools we've been _____ have been very special.

2 The Yetties used to have an agent, or manager, _____ whom they got their bookings.

3 Here is the list of videos we can select _____ .

4 This is the bit of homework I need some help _____ .

5 Where was the language school you went _____ ?

6 Which was the newspaper you saw the advert _____ ?

7 What was the organisation _____ which your exchange visit to the USA was arranged?

8 You need to understand the country _____ which you work.

9 There's a book written by children called Cry for Our beautiful World, the aim _____ which is to bring to adults' attention the state of the world _____ which we live today.

10 He was asked to bring enough food for six, instead _____ which he arrived with flowers!

11 This is the type of notebook the school provides you _____ .

12 They hated the weather in England, but nevertheless enjoyed the language course and the English family _____ whose house they stayed.

Write a list of the advantages of staying in an English family rather than in a hotel.

> The Grammar Word for this unit is <u>if</u>.
> See Grammar Book page 56.

BBC Foreign correspondent

Bob Jobbins BBC correspondent

a Which preposition fits in each space?

at	by	for	in	of	on	to	with

The job
External Services

BBC External Services broadcast _____ the world _____ English and 36 other languages _____ over 100 hours every day. They are financed _____ parliamentary grants-in-aid. The government prescribes the languages which are broadcast and the length _____ time each one is _____ the air, but editorial control of what is broadcast rests _____ the BBC.

Programmes are designed _____ give news and reports _____ world events, and project a broad picture _____ Britain's life and thought.

The main programmes _____ English is the World Service, _____ the air continuously _____ 24 hours a day and addressed _____ peak listening times _____ all parts _____ the world.

for	from	in	of	on	until

_____ fourteen years, _____ his promotion _____ 1987, you would hear Bob Jobbins reporting _____ different parts _____ the world _____ the BBC World Service.

b Write questions about the texts above to which these could be the answers.

a They stand for British Broadcasting Corporation.

b 37 including English.

c by grants from Parliament.

d No, it controls only what languages are broadcast and the length of time each is on the air, not the content of the programmes, nor the opinions expressed.

e No, they also give a broad picture of life and thought in Britain.

f the World Service.

g a BBC World Service correspondent.

Language study

a Where could these words and phrases fit in this extract from Bob Jobbin's interview?

actually	if you like	more	of course
particular	possible	really	

Does a foreign correspondent, when he's _____ working, specialise in one aspect of the country? In economics, for example, or politics, or foreign policy?

No, not, _____. I think it's _____ a question of specializing in the country in which you work. So you have to become an expert on that _____ country. Or more usually, er, the countries in the region . . .

And within those very large geographical limits, er, you have to try to know absolutely everything on every _____ subject, which _____ is impossible. And so, what you come back to is, _____, the basic skill of journalism . . .

b In the extract below, underline the phrases that mean <u>all</u> or <u>whole</u>.

. . . it's nowadays very common for foreign correspondents to cover a complete region. So, for example, you could be based in Cairo and cover the entire Middle East, or in Buenos Aires and cover the whole continent of South America, or in Singapore and cover all of South East Asia. And within those very large geographical limits, you have to try to know everything on every possible subject, which of course is impossible . . .

Grammar

Noun before noun

Write a phrase which explains each noun group in the following sentences. The first one has been done for you.

a He runs a <u>film production company</u>.

A company which produces films.

b She quickly became a <u>media success</u>.

_____

c There's no <u>government control</u> over <u>programme content</u>.

_____

d They are advertising for <u>economics advisers</u> and <u>programme production assistants</u>.

_____

e The <u>time limit</u> for applying is this Friday.

_____

f He started off as a <u>tea boy</u> and he now owns a <u>£250,000 pound house</u>.

a Points to remember

Write each sentence out again starting with the words given, so that it means the same.

a Bob Jobbins mentioned five points to remember.
   There were five...

b Once the information is available, it has to be written in an interesting way.
   It is important...

c It must be easily understood.
   It must be easy...

d While a newspaper reader can turn back and reread a sentence or two, the radio listener has only one chance.
   Unlike the newspaper reader...

e Only a limited number of facts can be contained in one sentence.
   One sentence should...

f Any vital information necessary to understand the latest development should be presented at the start of the report.
   The correspondent should begin the...

g A cheerful voice... would be sadly out of place for a report of a plane crash.
   If a correspondent is reporting...

h This would also confuse and distract the listener.
   In addition, the listener...

b Reading and summary

In the USA, TV news-readers are free to give their own opinions about the news they are reading. In the UK, news-readers are supposed to be completely impartial.

Read this extract from an article in a British newspaper.

Our TV men lag behind America's film-star salaries

The difference in power between British and American newsmen is reflected in their salaries and lifestyles.

John Schubeck, for example, rakes in £250,000 a year as CBS anchorman in Los Angeles.

Fred Dinenage, co-presenter of the TVS evening news programme Coast to Coast earns just £50,000.

John checks messages on the car-phone in his Mercedes as he cruises along the freeway to the CBS studios in Hollywood for a 2.30 pm start.

His wife and five children are back at home in their million-dollar house complete with tennis court and swimming pool.

Fred has a £250,000 modern detached house with a paddock and two horses in the Hampshire village of Hambledon.

He drives to Southampton in a Range Rover to get to work at 9.30 am while his American opposite number is still asleep.

Fred, 45, started his career in journalism as a tea-boy with the Birmingham Evening Mail.

He worked for a news agency at Doncaster and the Brighton Evening Argus before getting his break in television co-hosting a show with actress Diane Keen.

LUXURIES

Fred worked as a TV freelance for 18 years on quiz shows and children's programmes, with stints at World of Sport, and covered the Olympic Games in Munich and Moscow for ITN.

He describes his lifestyle as comfortable, and earns enough to pay for life's little luxuries like a Harley Street doctor, a BMW for his wife Bez, and private education for their six-year-old twins, Christopher and Sarah. He also has a 16-year-old daughter Caroline.

"A fortune teller once told me I would earn a lot of money but I would have to work for it," he says.

"It would be nice to earn what they get in America, but I look at my house and job and I feel I'm comfortably off. I think I've been very lucky to survive in this business for so long.

John Schubeck is 53, a slightly greying handsome man, and even though he rarely leaves the studios before midnight, he has time to run his own film editing and production companies.

Like Fred, he has been in the business a long time—30 years—after switching from medicine half-way through his course at Michigan University and spending four years at law school.

He has been a broadcaster in New York and Los Angeles for more than ten years.

Read this summary about Fred Dinenage. How many mistakes can you find in it? Write sentences correcting three of the mistakes.

e.g. *Fred Dinenage is 45 years old, not 55.*

55 year-old Fred Dinenage, the co-presenter of Britain's BBC evening news earns around £50,000 a year. He lives with his wife and four children in a £250,000 semi-detached house in Hambledon, Hampshire. He lives a comfortable life. His wife drives a Range Rover and his children are privately educated. Fred started work as a journalist in Brighton then moved to a newspaer in Doncaster before becoming a freelance television journalist 18 years ago.

Write a short summary like this about John Schubeck.

> **The Grammar Word for this unit is can/could.**
> **See Grammar Book page 54.**

Unit 15 Newspapers

[149] ## Mystery headlines

Here are five jumbled headlines followed by the opening sentences of five news stories. Reorder the words in the headlines to make one headline for each news story.

> ### blast cinema in kills two

> ### 'welcome' mail junk

> ### fine parking £4,000

> ### baby Bouncing

> ### Pay British workers union subscriptions lower

> **bounce** When something such as a ball bounces, it springs upwards or away immediately after hitting the ground . . .
> **bouncing** if you refer to a child as a bouncing baby you mean they are looking very healthy.
> **junk mail** is advertising and publicity materials that you receive through the post even though you have not asked for them.
> **A subscription** is an amount of money that you pay regularly to a society, charity or campaign in order to belong to it or to help the charity or campaign.

Now read the first lines of the news items.
For each one

a Write the headline from above which fits best.

b Write two questions that you think should be answered in the complete item.

a _____

> TWO people were killed and more than 20 injured when a bomb

_____

b _____

> Most people like getting junk mail, and more than two-thirds open and

_____

c _____

> **B**RITISH workers pay a smaller proportion of their earnings to their trade unions then workers in West Germany, France and Italy, according to a

_____

d _____

> A TRAFFIC warden who was hit by a car after ordering the driver to move was awarded £4,000 damages in the High Court.

_____

e _____

> A BABY who fell on his head after slipping from a bedroom window

_____

[151] ## Language study

Reporting words

Make reporting phrases by filling in the missing letters.

a The Government have __nn__ __nc__d their decision to . . .

b __cc__rd__ng to a Government spokesman, . . .

c An __nn__ __nc__m__nt made by a senior official . . .

d It is cl__ __m__d that over 2 million . . .

e There have been r__p__rts of renewed fighting on the border despite r__m__ __rs that peace talks are even now being held . . .

f A st__t__m__nt issued by the Home Office last night s__ys that . . .

g Despite r__m__ __rs of renewed violence . . .

h Paul Stickelt is __ll__g__d to have escaped . . .

i It is b__l__ __v__d that he was helped . . .

Which examples contain words that imply that the news may not be true?

Dictionary skills

British workers pay lower union subscriptions

BRITISH workers pay a smaller proportion of their earnings to their trade unions than workers in West Germany, France and Italy, according to a survey published today.

The union magazine Labour Research says contribu-tions are about half those in West Germany and two-thirds of those for France and Italy. Only in the UK do most union members pay a fixed-rate contribution irres-pective of earnings. Else-where, contributions are fre-quently a direct percentage.

Contributions among the 21 unions with over 100,000 members range from 62p a week for the shopworkers' Usdaw to more than £2 for the print union NGA. The majority cluster around 90p – about 0.5 per cent of earnings.

Read the following report. Then fill in the correct names on the block graph above. Which words from the report are defined in the dictionary entries below?

> **CONTRIBUTION** _____ part of your wages that you pay to the government or your company etc.
> A _____ amount, position, pat-tern, method etc always stays the same.
> If something is true or if it happens _____ other things, those things do not affect it.
> _____ is the number of things or people that form more than half of a larger group.
> a _____ of a whole thing is part of it.
> _____ is an organisation of workers that represents them and that has the aim of improving such things as the working conditions of its members.

Are these statements true or false?

a In Britain, nearly all members pay the same union fee, no matter how much they earn.

b In other European countries, members often pay fixed-rate contributions.

c A very small proportion of British workers pay contributions that are a direct percentage of their earnings.

d There are 21 trade unions in Britain today.

e Only 21 unions in the UK have over 100,000 members.

f Approximately 21 unions have over 100,000 members.

g 62p a week is the lowest contribution paid.

h £2 a week is the highest contribution paid.

i The average contribution is about 90p a week.

j 90p would average out at 0.5 per cent of members' earnings.

k Usdaw and NGA are names of unions with over 100,000 members.

News in brief:

Who what when where why?

Sometimes it helps you to understand or write a text if you see it as a dialogue, giving answers to questions.

The news item *Train Cut* (Student's Book section 154) is used here as an example. Write in appropriate question words, with a verb.

_____ it about?
– a strike
_____ on strike?
– Underground workers
_____ they on strike?
– they are demanding a pay rise
_____ was the result of the strike?
– the number of rush hour trains was cut by half.

Now do the same with this item. Write questions which could be answered by the words underlined.

How did the baby fall on his head?
Where did he land?

> A BABY who fell on his head <u>after slipping from a bedroom window on to a concrete path</u>, escaped with <u>only slight injuries</u>. <u>Two-year-old Rikki Miles of Bulwell, Notts</u> was playing <u>near the window 15 feet up</u> when he fell. He is being kept in hospital for a few days <u>for observation</u> but apart from a bump on his head, <u>he is unhurt</u>.

Grammar

Wh- + to

The phrases in the second part of each sentence have been mixed up. Rearrange them.

a Some people hate getting junk mail, but – to – to – can't – who – find out – complain

b Sometimes every household gets the same mail because – don't – companies – to – to – who – send – advertising materials ¬ know – really – their

c Some people ask the Post Office – stop – how – junk mail – to them – to – being sent

d If you wanted to stop junk mail being delivered to your home – would – know – to – write – where – you, or – ask – who – to ?

e I recently – what – do – found out – to.

f Send it all back unopened, but the problem is, – time – find – how – the – to

g And the other difficulty is how to distinguish between important mail and junk mail, in other words – which – knowing – send back – to – and which – open and read – to

> **The Grammar Word for this unit is must.**
> **See Grammar Book page 57.**

Unit 16
What style radio news?

Who said/did what?

Read the transcript of part of the news broadcast about the water shortage.

All the words denoting people have been taken out. Fill the gaps. You will need to use some words more than once.

Then practise reading the news item out loud, in the same way as Bob Jobbins did.

the authorities	the farmers
the Government	the militants
the Minister of Agriculture	the ordinary public
the victims	

INTERVIEWER
But _____ only yesterday denied this, _____ said in Parliament that no further permission would be given for building on farm land, and that _____ was committed to supporting _____ in their drive to produce more food...

BOB JOBBINS
Yes, _____ is publicly committed to protecting farmland. But _____ themselves seem unconvinced. Unless _____ do something to settle this fight over water, _____ are going to believe those who say _____ is more interested in the future of the city than it is in farming and food production, and all the signs are that _____ in POW and other groups are prepared to fight. And, as we've seen, _____ are likely to be _____, who at the moment have no choice but to seek water where they can find it.

162 *Language study*

Classifying

Think of ways to complete these paragraphs, using the suggestions given. Write each one out in full.

a   Not all learner drivers learn at the same speed. Some . . . Others . . . While a few . . .

b   People differ when it comes to attending job interviews. Some people, especially those who have been out of work for a long time, ... However others . . .

c   Meeting new people can be a terrifying experience, for adults as well as children. The majority of adults . . . A few people however . . .

d   The Yetties have done a lot of travelling. Mostly, their trips . . . But once, . . .

163 Current affairs

Questions and answers

Here is a follow up to the Lilliburlero news story you read in section 161 in your Student's Book.

"Mrs Etty, the Dorset farmer's wife who disappeared mysteriously five days ago has returned to her husband in similarly mysterious circumstances. Questioned by reporters as to her whereabouts over the last five days, and asked to comment on the speculation that she had joined a group of devil-worshippers, Mrs Etty replied "I think the devil's got enough trouble down there without wanting me as well. I'm a strong-willed woman you know. Even the devil himself wouldn't have it all his own way with me.""

Rewrite it as a question and answer story. Start like this:

INTERVIEWER
Can you tell us, Bob, where Mrs Etty has been for the last five days?

BOB JOBBINS
Well, . . .

Grammar

a Fronting information

Using facts from the above extract, and what you already know about the situation, make up a long sentence to open a news item (like the one in your Student's Book, about farmers. Use this framework:

Having _____ _____, local farmers, worried _____, are preparing to _____

b Conflict and dispute: prepositions

You can use <u>with</u> to indicate that two or more people are fighting, arguing or competing with each other. e.g. ... a naval war with France ...... a row with my brother.

<u>Between</u> can be used to express the relationship between people, organisations etc. who are involved in a fight or disagreement with each other, e.g. ... the growing conflict between East and West ...

You can use over/about/regarding/concerning to indicate the source or cause of some problem e.g. We had a dreadful argument over the children.

Rearrange these letters to form words describing a conflict of some sort:

ruetagmn: A R G U M E N T _____

dsueipt: _____

orw: _____

fgtih: _____

btleat: _____

arw: _____

ureqarl: _____

Write three sentences about a quarrel or argument you once had. Who was it with? What was it about?

Write three sentences about a battle or a dispute. Who was it between? What was the cause?

Make six sentences based on the patterns in the table below and complete them with your own ideas. X and Y can stand for personal names as well as official bodies.

The	argument dispute row fight battle conflict quarrel	with between	the Y Y the X and Y X and Y	over regarding	water supplies boundaries land use sale of cigarettes use of the telephone	has been	set in motion again brought to a head/ an end	by the ... through ...

Dictionary skills

Drive, run, sweep

What could the other meanings of these words be? Use a dictionary to check. Then study how the verbs are used in the examples given below.

... supporting farmers in their drive to produce more food.
Fire swept through a hospital ...
... an incident connected with the long running dispute over water supplies.

GIVE THE KITCHEN FLOOR A SWEEP, COULD YOU?

The kitchen really needs sweeping.
The driving rain blew into my face.
Rain swept across the country ...
The economic crisis drove many small companies into debt, even those run by experienced directors.
Their five children nearly drove me mad.
The Mousetrap – 36th year – London's longest running play.

He settled down at the table, casually sweeping all the papers on to the floor.
Accused by everybody? That's rather a sweeping statement!
Honest, I don't understand what you're driving at. What do you mean?

Find words or phrases from the above to complete these sentences:

The continuous noise of the traffic kept us awake and

_____

She came out of the underground and was almost _____ off her feet by the football crowds rushing past.

95% without work?. You shouldn't make _____ like that!

Sadly his company was driven out of business by the larger companies, despite being

_____ .

> **The Grammar Word for this unit is <u>by</u>.**
> **See Grammar Book page 54.**

Unit 17
All for the love of . . .

Influence

a Reading and vocabulary

The letter below was written to the problem page of a magazine. Where could these phrases fit?

> to go along
> going around to her parents.
> my problem is
> she works with
> if I talk about
> the opposite of what she says

My possessive friend

_____ _____ my best friend who has become very possessive about me. She likes to spend most nights either visiting my house or with me _____. She doesn't like me to have any other friends and if I talk about anyone at work she gets all cold and upset. In some ways this wouldn't worry me, but she does _____

A couple of nights a week she goes to the disco or the pub with the girls _____ _____ but has never once asked me _____.

Who do you think is the person being influenced: the writer or the best friend:? _____

b Composition

The reply the magazine offered consisted of sentences which contained these words and phrases. Make them into full sentences that would be suitable for the reply. They are in the right order. Add words and change the verb forms where necessary.

1 a true friend   someone who   care and who   want   best for you.

2 afraid   this girl   not suitable

3 doesn't want   you have other friends   and yet   she   go out friends   without you

4 you think   acceptable way so-called friend   behave ?

5 time   you make   effort   increase your circle of friends   and stop   rely on girl.

How many weddings?

Question practice

Read the story, then write the following questions in full.

Here comes the bride – again

American Carole Roble has more than beaten Elizabeth Taylor's record of seven wedding ceremonies. She's been married 43 times – but it's always to the same man, her husband Richard. Since their first wedding in Youngstown, Ohio, in 1969, Richard and Carole have been married by ministers, judges, rabbis, preachers and even a Navajo Indian. "We call it a renewable option," says Richard. "I keep proposing, she accepts and we go through the whole thing again." Life must be just one long honeymoon for this lucky couple. ■

What nationality
_____

Whose record
_____

How many
_____

How many
_____

Who
_____

When
_____

Who
_____

How
_____

What
_____

. . . do you think
_____

Write the word or phrase in the story which stands for:

ask someone to marry you _____

choice _____

another ceremony _____

fortunate man and wife _____

Language study ············

Phrases with prepositions

These are all sentences from the story about Selina.
Fill the blanks with a preposition from the box.

> about behind down in of on through to with

1 He could never have guessed what he was letting
   himself _____ for.
2 Things normally went according _____
   plan.
3 He proposed marriage _____ beautiful
   blonde Selina Rigden-Hodge.
4 Set _____ a career, they banned any
   prospect _____ marriage.
5 ... hired detectives to track her _____.
6 ... made her a ward of court _____ a
   desperate attempt to bring her home.
7 Now, _____ the adventure some months
   _____ them ...
8 We've been _____ an awful lot ... but it's all
   been worth it.
9 You could certainly write a good book
   _____ what we've been _____.
10 I've got my career to think _____.
11 We just want to be left _____ our own
   now ...

Grammar ············

Past participles

Complete these in any way you like to make
sentences. The first two have been done for you.

a Rejected by his friends, he
   turned to his brother for advice.

b Partly destroyed during the war, the city walls
   have now been rebuilt in the original style.

c Given the choice of white or brown bread, I
   would

   _____

d Worried by the strange noises from the
   neighbour's house, he

   _____

e Excited at the thought of the holidays starting,
   the children

   _____

f Designed by Pierre and made by Alexis, this
   beautiful wedding dress

   _____

g Completed three months earlier than planned, the
   new motorway

   _____

Grammar ············

a When had equals if ...

Finish each of these sentences so that it means the
same as the sentence printed before it.

a I would have explained everything to you had you
   asked me.
      If you ...
b I would have collected you from the station if I
   had known you were coming.
      Had I ...
c If you had only told me I could have helped you.
      Had you only ...
d If I had thought of it I would have called you
   earlier.
      Had ...
e He would never have gone had he known what
   was going to happen.
      If ...
f We'd have enjoyed the film more if it had been a
   little shorter.
      Had ...

b Related words

The word in capitals can be used to form a word that
fits in the space. Fill each space in this way.

a Their first _____ ended in disaster MARRY
b As the couples grew older they became
   _____ similar INCREASE
c In some cases, husbands and wives change
   _____ EQUAL
d The husband gets more like his wife, but it's
   _____ true to say that she will get more like
   him. EQUAL
e It's not a good basis for _____ between
   parents and new son-in-law. FRIEND
f _____ there was no note, I would have
   contacted the police. ASSUME
g In the world market, there is fierce _____
   for sales. COMPETE
h The terms of their _____ proposal to sell
   world-wide were quite acceptable. BASE
i Was it in 1954 that Nigeria declared
   _____? INDEPENDENT
j Smoking is now _____ on the London
   underground. BAN

> The Grammar Word for this unit is **for**.
> See Grammar Book page 55.

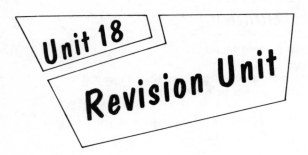

News round-up

182

a Questions to predict content

Read <u>Walk on water</u>. Do you think it's possible?

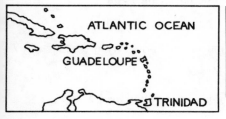

WALK ON WATER
Frenchman Rene Bricka arrived in Trinidad claiming to have 'walked' across the Atlantic from Tenerife on polyester floats strapped to his feet.

Observer 5/6/88

After reading it, what questions spring to your mind? Complete seven sentences from this table to make queries about things you'd like to know.
e.g.

I wonder how he slept.

It doesn't say	how . . .
I wonder	where . . .
I can't imagine	what . . .
We aren't told	how long . . .
Are we told	how far . . .
Does it say	who . . .
A longer report might explain	why . . .

b Reading practice

Now read this second news item about Rene Bricka, and answer as many of your own questions as possible. Then answer questions 1–3.

MEANWHILE, AT SEA . . .

Rene strides out across the Atlantic

A FRENCHMAN has travelled 45 miles in his bid to *walk* across the Atlantic.

Rene Bricka set off from the Canaries on Friday, travelling on 15ft polyester skis and propelling himself with a single oar. He is towing a rubber dinghy in which he sleeps, but has taken no food for the 3,750-mile trip.

He plans to live off fish caught from the sea, and hopes to reach Guadeloupe in 10 weeks. His girlfriend, Marie-Rose Regnier, said yesterday: "He has a lot of guts."

Today 4/4/88

1 When it was probably written?

   a 10 weeks after he reached the West Indies.
   b shortly after he set out from the Canaries.
   c 10 weeks after he out from the Canaries.
   d shortly before before he arrived in Trinidad.

2 How many miles would Rene have had to average in one day?

   a 37.5 miles
   b 45 miles
   c 53.5 miles
   d 15 miles

Write a sentence explaining how to calculate this.

3 Which of these must he have taken with him? Which might he have taken? Write what you think beside each item, giving a reason for each one. Finally add two more items, and explain why you think he had them.

Food supplies: . . .

Fresh water: . . .

Containers to catch water in . . .

Something to sleep on or in . . .

a fishing line or net . . .

a cooking stove . . .

a light . . .

a radio . . .

Good news and bad news

183

a Which

Make sentences about these things using these prepositions with the word <u>which</u> or <u>whom</u> :

about	after	during	in	with

He was pulling a rubber boat in which he slept

   a He was pulling a rubber boat . . . (sleep).
   b It should be a 10 week journey . . . (meet/ girlfriend)
   c He had a fishing line . . . (catch fish)
   d He also needed a container . . . (collect rainwater)
   e He really missed his girlfriend, Marie-Rose, . . . (think a lot)
   f His girlfriend took part in an interview, . . . (was asked/embarrassing questions)

Now write each one again, ending with a preposition.
e.g.
He was pulling a rubber boat to sleep in.
He was pulling a rubber boat which he slept in.

b What facts does a report give us?

38

Read this report. Find another word from the text for each of these. They are in the right order.

asking urgently _____
pay for part of _____
wealthier _____
medicines _____
make-up _____
areas _____
rainforest _____

Indonesia urges Western countries to share cost of conserving tropical rainforests

INDONESIA is pressing the industrialised countries to help share the cost of preserving the world's tropical rainforest.

The Environment Minister, Mr Emil Salim, said the richer countries of the world which could make most use of the rainforests of Brazil, Zaire and Indonesia for drugs and cosmetics must be ready to help pay for conserving huge tracts of equatorial jungle.

Guardian 6/6/88

How many short sentences can you make out of the second sentence?

Mr Emil Salim is the Environment Minister. Rainforests can be useful sources of drugs. There are rainforests in Brazil.
Can you make 10 more?

187 Argument is war

Words with metaphorical meanings

Which word will fit in all the sentences in each set? You may need to change the form of the word.

adopt	attack	balance	pour	sweep

a   If Jack's injuries do turn out to be the result of a deliberate _____, it will ...

The farmers have _____ the government for failing to protect their water supplies.

b   ... send a cheque to cover the _____ of their fees.

The country had a delicately _____ economy.

c   They quickly _____ each other's personality traits.

The parents of _____ children have special problems.

The government wanted to _____ the new scheme immediately.

d   Can you _____ me a drink?

Together with thousands of citizens, the world's press _____ into the presidential palace.

It was _____ with rain.

e   A strong wind was _____ down the valley.

Romeo Paul _____ Roedean beauty off her feet!

Language study

a   Make questions which could be answered by using the words underlined.

> **Junk mail 'welcome'**
> Most people like getting junk mail, and more than two-thirds open and read everything that comes through their letter boxes, according to figures published by the Post Office yesterday. The average household receives almost 30 items of mail each month.

Guardian 6/6/88

b   Noun groups: fronting information

Use the information given below (in any order) to make sentences giving more information about the nouns underlined.

A man saw and reported an accident in his factory.

   Man:
   He works on an assembly line.
   aged 45
   experienced in factory floor safety
   Jim Morrison

Two children found an empty bag that police now say had been used by a thief to carry jewelry .

   Children:
   sisters
   7 and 9
   Warwick Rd, Eastham
   Sara and Rachel Moon
   playing by a stream near home

   jewelry:
   stolen
   worth over £5000
   owned by Mrs Liz Carey
   had belonged to great grandmother
   from a house in Starbottom

190 Detective work

Sources – known, unknown or implied?

Find the sources of as many of the news items on these pages as possible. Where the sources are not mentioned, where could we suppose the reporter got the news from? Make a list of the sources.

> The Grammar Word for this unit is <u>will</u>.
> See Grammar Book page 61.

39

Unit 19
Spot the hoax

196 Hero

Practice in verb forms

These are extracts from the news story you read in Student's Book 2. Complete them using the correct forms of the verbs in capitals.

SPIDERMAN TO RESCUE

a

Fireman Lionel Lovisio _____ HAIL as a spiderman hero last night.

He _____ LEAP from the roof of a Paris apartment block to save a lovesick woman who _____ JUMP out of her fifth-floor window.

It was the kind of feat that normally _____ BELONG to the pages of the cartoon character. Lovisio, _____ WEAR a harness and line, actually _____ CATCH 25 year old Jeanne Charmean before she _____ HIT the ground.

Jeanne _____ LEAN out of the window for several hours _____ THREATEN to jump. "My lover _____ LEAVE me," she shouted.

"I'm alone with a small baby, and I _____ LOSE my job."

---

b

After five hours of fruitless _____ CHAT with the priest and the police, the woman _____ CLIMB out on to the window sill.

Lovisio _____ WATCH her ever movement. Then she jumped to what _____ BE her death. The fireman _____ JUMP too.

Later Jeanned said: "I must _____ BE out of my mind."

---

198 Reincarnation

Reading skills and sentence building

a Arrange the jumbled phrases in the right order to complete the first paragraph of this report.

Many researchers believe in reincarnation. And youngsters often seem to have a clear memory of past lives. Writer Guy Lyon Playfair, who has investigated reincarnation for many years, says: "When children first begin to talk they may . . .

_____

_____

or people/places/speak of/people/or/they've never been to/they've never met

---

They could be talking about previous lives. There have been several . . .

_____

_____

who died young/astonishing cases/to the same parents/of children/apparently being reborn

b Complete each sentence using and adding to the key-words below. You may need to make other changes to the key words.

John Pollock believes his twin daughters, Gillian and Jennifer are the reincarnation . . .

_____

_____

first two daughters   kill   car crash

Joanne was 11 and her sister Jacqueline six when . . .

_____

_____

die   way   church   near home   Hexham, Northumberland.

A year later, John's wife Florence . . .

_____

_____

tell   pregnant

"I was certain .

_____

_____

have   twins   although   doctors unlikely   says John.

Florence gave birth to identical girls on October 4, 1958.

(This report is continued in Practice Book section 202)

Grammar

Whenever:

Composition practice

Think of a village or town where you used to live, or a place you used to go to regularly on holiday. Use some of the sentence frames below to write a paragraph about what you used to do there, and what it was like. About 130 words.

When we were . . . we used to . . . (live in/go and spend week-ends with/go to . . . on holiday) . . .

Whenever the weather was . . . (good/bad/hot/wet), we would . . . and . . .

There were . . . (several/one or two/a lot of) other people . . . (like us/our age/) who also lived/went there too, and we would sometimes . . .

We often went . . . (walking/shopping/fishing . . .)(in/near/up the . . .)

Another thing we occasionally did was . . .

We always had a good time, and hated the thought of . . . (going home/leaving the area/leaving our friends.)

Dictionary skills

Read this continuation of the story about reincarnation from section 198, and try to guess what the missing words could be. Find suitable words from the definitions below that could be used to fill the spaces left here. Some words will be used more than once.

> A **birthmark** is a mark on someone's skin that has been there since they were born.
> If you are **convinced** of something, you are sure that it is true and correct.
> A **doll** is a child's toy which looks like a small person or baby.
> **Evidence** is anything you see, experience, read, or are told that causes you to believe that something is true or has really happened.
> An **expert** is a person who has studied a particular subject and knows a lot about it.
> A **scar** is a line or mark on the skin which is left after a wound has healed.
> A **toy** is an object that children play with, for example a doll or a model car.

In a few days a _____ appeared on Jennifer's left hip, exactly where Jacqueline had a similar mark. Then John noticed a white _____ on her forehead. Jacqueline had one there too, from when she cut herself at the age of two. When the girls were nearly three the Pollocks found a box of _____ that had belonged to their dead sisters.

"There were two _____," John says. "When Jennifer saw the one that had been Jacqueline's she said, 'That's my Mary.' She'd never seen the _____ before. It was the one Jacqueline had called Mary.

"Gillian picked up the other _____, which had been Joanna's, and said, 'That's my dolly that we had a long time ago.'"

Those and other happenings _____ the Pollocks that the twins are reincarnations of their dead daughters.

A growing number of _____ have come to believe that only reincarnation can explain these strange cases.

"It is very possible that it happens," says Dr David Stevenson, a senior lecturer at Liverpool School of Tropical Medicine, who closely follows these cases.

"When young children seem to recall past lives it is very difficult to put it down to anything else but reincarnation. The _____ is very strong."

Review

Nouns, verbs or both?

Complete the table below to make noun/verb pairs by putting the appropriate form in the blank space.

NOUN	VERB
display	display
exposure	*expose*
_____	block
imagination	_____
_____	mystify
_____	swing
threat	_____
_____	examine
belongings	_____
chat	_____

> **The Grammar Word for this unit is _that_.**
> **See Grammar Book page 59.**

Unit 20
Off to sea!

Big ships small ships

Reading composition

Read these extracts about travelling to the Isle of Wight, then write some advice for the following travellers, about which ferries to take, and how to travel onward. Give reasons for your advice.

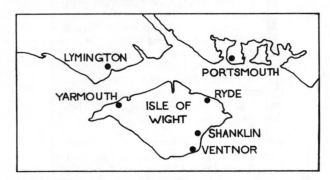

Take a Sealink route to the Isle of Wight and start your holiday in style.

With a choice of routes and a fleet of purpose-built vessels, Sealink really is the only way to travel.

PORTSMOUTH – FISHBOURNE CAR FERRY
A 35 minute journey aboard one of the three largest ferries making the Isle of Wight crossing.

LYMINGTON – YARMOUTH CAR AND PASSENGER FERRY
The fastest car ferry crossing to the Island – only 30 minutes.

PORTSMOUTH – RYDE PASSENGER FERRY
Less than 15 minutes aboard one of our superb new catamarans and you're there.

On car ferry crossings passengers can enjoy a drink or snack from the bar and buffet or simply relax and take in the ever changing Solent scene from one of the observation decks whilst Sealink speed you across to your holiday island.
It's fast, it's comfortable, it's first class all the way.

With Sealink, the Isle of Wight is around half an hour away across the Solent. An Island in the sun, with miles of golden beaches lapped by warm, blue waters; rolling countryside, historic castles and manor houses, theme parks and craft centres; vineyards and gardens, pubs and restaurants. There's something for everyone and there's no better way to travel there than with Sealink.

TAKE YOUR BICYCLE FREE!
Cycles are conveyed free of charge on most rail and sea services to Ryde and Yarmouth (subject to availability of space).

There are approximately 500 miles of road and leafy lanes to explore, with a choice of Youth Hostels, camp sites, hotels and guest houses to help you make the most of your Island cycling holiday.

Please note there are no facilities for bicycles on Isle of Wight trains between Ryde Pier and Shanklin.

GROUP TRAVEL
Special group tickets are available for parties of 10 or more travelling together between Portsmouth and Ryde.

MR POLEDEN
A tired, impatient business man with a sports car who wants to get to his luxury hotel in Shanklin as quickly as possible on the Friday evening. Wants a very relaxing week end.

MISS LACY AND FRIEND
Students, intending to spend a week touring the Isle of Wight on their bicycles. Interested in sightseeing and swimming. Not much money

THE PEACOCKS AND THE SACKVILLES
Two families (one of 5, one of 6) planning to holiday together with small children and dog and children's bicycles on roof of one of the cars. Driving from the West of England. Don't mind how long the ferry takes, but don't like driving very much. They have a guest house booked in Ventnor.

Dictionary skills

More uses of new words

atmosphere	calm	creep
delicate	emerge	moderately
rough	row	deck

These words, which appeared in the first episode of *Dip in the Pool*, can also be used in other ways. Find a sentence, or two, where they could fit. Use a dictionary if necessary. You may need to change the form of the words.

a   'Don't make so much noise! _____ down, all of you."

b   'I prefer these flowers – they are so small and _____.' 'Mm – they have a very _____ scent, too.'

c   'No wind today, so the sea should be _____ enough.'
'Good thing too. Yesterday it was really _____. Awful!

d   'Her health is not good – she's always been rather _____ in fact.'

e   A small figure _____ slowly from the bedroom and _____ downstairs without a sound.

f   'The Shades is my favourite disco – it has great _____. Very friendly. And _____ priced, too. Some are so expensive.'

g   There were two _____ of small boats, lining the harbour; and one larger boat with passengers sitting out on _____, chatting.

h   After five months of doubt and mystery, and waiting for more details, the truth finally _____.

Language study

Verbs ending in -ing

Complete these sentences with phrases using a verb ending in -ing . The first one is done for you.

a   They felt the whole ship _rolling_ in the storm.

b   The worst thing about being on a ship in rough weather is _____

c   But I normally enjoy _____ .

d   Is that someone at the front door? I thought I heard _____

e   After bumping into me and making me drop everything, this man came _____ back to me, _____ 'Oh sorry! I must have been _____ , I simply didn't see you _____ !"

f   _____ is not one of my favourite sports, but I do occasionally go _____ .

g   Work out how much money you have to spend before _____ .

h   He telephoned me immediately on/after _____ .

i   Did you see someone _____ a bit ago?

j   Don't start _____ there's not time now.

k   _____ 18th floor, as we do, you get a really good view all over the town.

l   But we do get tired of _____ stairs, and the lifts are always _____ .

Dip in the pool

Weather

Read the following weather forecasts carefully. One is for April, the other is for early June. Can you guess which is which?

> VERY similar to yesterday. Scotland will remain cool and cloudy with rain at times, and this could fall as sleet or snow on the mountains. The rest of the British Isles will have another dry day with plenty of sunshine. It will become increasingly cloudy in the South with, perhaps, a few spots of rain near the coast by evening. Outlook: Little change – Scotland will continue cloudy with rain at times, dry and sunny elsewhere, except, perhaps, in the extreme South.

Daily Mail

> Outlook: Monday will start dry across much of southern Britain, but there will be rain in many northern areas. During Tuesday there will be rain across much of the country for a time, to be followed on Wednesday by showers, some of which may be fairly heavy, particularly in central and eastern areas.

Observer

a   Underline all the words and phrases which refer to time , i.e. which tell us when to expect this particular weather.

b   Write down any words or phrases that express quantity , e.g. much of Southern Britain.

or degree e.g. became increasingly cloudy.

c   Fill in this table in note form. Only include relevant information.

	DAILY MAIL		OBSERVER	
Month				
	TODAY	TOMORROW	TODAY	TOMORROW
Scotland				
Northern Ireland				
Wales				
England				

> The Grammar Word for this unit is <u>on</u>.
> See Grammar Book page 58.

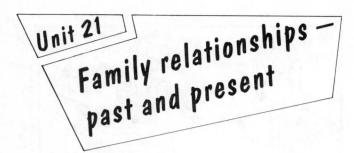

Unit 21 — Family relationships — past and present

215 In the old days

Children talking about dads

Guess what these children wrote about fathers.
Complete their comments by adding words from the
boxes. Then a comment about a father you know.

a

> Fathers are _____ right, and _____ they are
> not right, they are never _____ wrong.
> *Catherine aged 12.*

| actually | always | even if |

b

> In the eighteenth century a father was _____ on the
> outside and inside. By the twenties he was _____
> outside but _____ inside. Nowadays he is _____ both
> outside and inside. *Mark Wickham-Jones 13*

| hard | soft |

> **hard** Someone who is hard shows no kindness
> or sympathy towards other people. EG *She's
> very hard, no pity for anyone.*
> **soft** Someone who is soft is **5.1** kind and cares
> about other people's feelings **5.3** not strict
> enough.

c Can you work out how this one ended?
Re-arrange the words below to complete it.

> My father at lunch time says, 'Stop making that noise',
> _____!
> *Patricia 9*

| than | noise | anyone | making | else | more |

d Write this out again, changing or adding
punctuation, words, phrases or expressions to
make it easier to understand.

> My daddy has naughty habits they are.
> Daddy says that Mommy has got is keys
> but Mommy says she hasn't and
> Daddy says she has so Mommy
> says Look in your pocket so Daddy
> looks in his pocket and all that
> time he had them in his
> pocket
> Tracey aged 8

217 Dip in the pool

Compositions

Write notes and useful phrases for one of these
compositions.

Bad weather for a journey

Think of a journey you were on when the weather
conditions were bad; either very wet, stormy, windy,
cold, or extremely hot, dry, dusty etc. Say how and
where you were travelling, and describe the effect the
weather had on you.

The lost keys

Write about a time when you or someone you know
lost or forgot a key. Who was involved? What
happened as a result? Did you ever find the key?

218 Grammar

Future in the past

**Read these examples. Which is positive and which is
negative?**

a Two years ago we were planning to go to the USA
for a holiday, to stay with some old friends, but in
the end it proved too expensive so we never
actually went.

b Some people we know from Africa wrote and said
they were intending to come to Europe, so we
invited them to stay with us in Wales, which they
did. It was great fun.

**Use ideas from the table to help you write seven
sentences, some negative, some positive. Add your
own ideas.**

| I we he she | was were | planning to just about to on the point of (-ing) . . . intending to going to supposed to . . . hoping to | travel to . . . leave for . . . buy a . . . meet up . . . | , so . . . , , , but . . . |

44

Like father like son: uses of conjunctions

a Read this article, then find a word to fill each blank. Write it in the space beside the text.

Like father, like son, like driving

Like many eight year olds, James Thompson likes going out for a drive with his dad. _____ most though, _____ James, from Walsall in the West Midlands, tells you he's going for a drive he means just that. _____ Dad Steve hops into his gleaming white Vauxhall Nova, James climbs into his own Vauxhall Nova, _____. James' car is a half-scale replica which his motor-mad father made. It has headlights, a horn, a radio _____ cruises at a top speed of 15mph. _____, the 100cc engine power mini marvel isn't the only one of its kind. _____ seeing how happy the car made James, Steve decided to step up production of the half-scale models at his Irmscher car company. _____ he's turning out many kids' dream of a Christmas present – complete with a £1,800 nightmare price tag for parents. ∎

after	like	now	and
surprisingly	too	unlike	when (2)

b Using the notes given, make full sentences about the story above.

a Like/most small boys,/James/Walsall/loves/cars.
b Unlike/most 8 year-olds/toy cars,/James/real one.

Like most small boys, James Thompson, from Walsall, simply loves cars.

Whereas most 8-year-olds play with toy cars, James actually owns a real one.

c As well as/toy cars,/James/Walsall/real one.
d Although/James/only 8,/drive/Vauxhaull Nova.
e When/Steve his Dad/goes/drive,/James/too.
f As a result/James/dad/Irmscher car company,/increase/production/half-scale cars.
g Steve/hope/Christmas presents,/in spite of/£1,800!
h Assuming/parents/wealthy/buy them/, company/might/profit.
i Although/in UK/supposed be 17/before allowed/drive motor vehicle, since/James/not drive/public roads,/not need/driving licence.

a Rewrite the following, changing them by putting in appropriate conjunctions. If you can, write two different versions of each.

e.g. Working in a car factory, Mr Thompson is able to produce his own half-scale models.

Because/since he works in …

As a result of working in …

a On seeing how happy James was with his car, he decided to make some more.

b Kids may dream about getting a car for Christmas. Their parents think only of the £1,800 nightmare price tag.

c Each car takes so long to make, and requires a high standard of workmanship. The price is not actually that bad.

b Make a noun out of the word underlined.

The children were underlined confused . In fact everyone was running round in great _____.

He was unconscious for 4 hours after the accident. He finally regained _____ at 5.30.

They walked out silently ; in fact there was total _____ everywhere.

The departing guests waved Goodbye. The passengers were called into the _____ lounge.

Flights were being announced continually. It was quite difficult to hear the _____.

Many people grew tense as it got later. You could feel the _____ in the air.

The apartment was light, airy and spacious . Plenty of _____ for extra furniture, books and so on.

> The Grammar Word for this unit is <u>with</u>.
> See Grammar Book page 61.

If you had three wishes . . .

Hopes and pleas for the future

Reading and vocabulary revision

Read these young people's pleas.

a   Choose which of these titles you prefer for the first one.

Can we cut down on petrol engines?
ELECTRIC CARS ARE CLEANER.
Breathing polluted air can kill us.

Think of an effective title for the others. Write it in the space provided.

b   Find a suitable place for these words.

campaign	development	destroying
efficiency	grow	report	products

I would push for the _____ of electric cars which have less or no petrol exhaust at all.   *Keiji Fujita, Japan*

Twenty per cent of the earth is very cold, twenty per cent very dry, twenty per cent is mountainous. Of the remaining forty per cent, about ten per cent has very little soil and rain fall. And mankind is busy _____ the rest.
                              Donald M. Phiri, Zambia

Of all forms of annoyance, noise is perhaps the most inescapable. Scientists _____ that, when animals are made to listen to noise they _____ unresponsive, erratic or violent. May not the same be true about us?
                              Hadia Malek El-Ashkar, 13, Egypt

On television I've seen the hunters killing and dismembering the whales with deadly _____, and it's a bloody, dirty shame. As one whale-lover put it, 'Nothing is wasted, except the whale's life.'
                              Billy Gorman, 17, USA

There are substitutes for whale _____ but none for whales themselves. Public pressure works. Because of an active public education _____, whaling operations in Australia have ended. Each of us can help save the whales by refusing to purchase any Japanese or Russian products. We can boycott Japanese products such as cars, motorcycles, televisions or stereos.
                              Lura Stoker, 14, USA

Dictionary skills

Words ending in -age .

Think what these words could mean, and use them to complete these sentences:

baggage	leakage	breakages
mileage	postage	shortage

a   All _____ must be paid for.

b   Ford Escort. 1987. Excellent condition. Low _____. 453215.

c   This recent lack of rain has resulted in severe water _____ in all areas.

d   I want to send this by airmail. What's the _____ to Japan?

e   When using my car for essential business, what _____ allowances can I claim?

f   I'm afraid you have 15 kilos of excess _____. You could send it unaccompanied air-freight; it'll be cheaper.

g   I'm afraid there must be a _____ in the fuel system. There's hardly any petrol left.

Where would you be likely to hear or see a–g above? Write the letter in the appropriate space below.

post office _____

notice in a china shop _____

new company employee to boss. _____

car service station _____

railway station _____

second-hand car advert _____

agricultural report _____

airport _____

If you had three wishes...

May-day wishes

In some countries May 1st is Labour Day. This is traditionally a day when all workers have a day's holiday in recognition of their work.

These working people, who all live in Singapore, were interviewed just before Labour Day and asked about their wishes.

Most of the time, our wish is their command, but today we try to turn the tables round to find out what wish they would most like to be granted.
A better job, a motor-cycle, more understanding – and honesty – from the people they serve.

a Can you work out who said which?

a Ramasay Palaniandi, 49, car-washer
b Wagiman Salam, 39, postman
c Lee Rin Ne, 20, receptionist
d Madam S Wong, cinema ticket seller
e Sopia Yusof Ibrahim, 22, car park attendant

1 I wish cinema-goers would control their tempers. When popular shows are sold out, the disappointed ones vent their anger on me: "What, sold out so soon?" they ask sarcastically, as if they don't believe me.

2 I have nothing to wish for. I am quite happy in my job. It is not very difficult and all my clients pay me on time.

3 I'd like a motor-cycle so that I can do my work faster. It's a six-day week for me, starting at 7 a.m. and not finishing till all my letters are delivered.

4 If only motorists would be more honest. Some, on the excuse that they'll only be five minutes, park without paying. About an hour later they pop out and some manage to slip away!

5 My co-workers are cheerful enough. It's the office that gets me down. I can't wait to move to new premises where I can make my surroundings more pleasant.

b Summarise the information above by completing these short reports.

Unlike 49 year old ... car washer, whose clients ... car park attendant ... reported that ... His May Day wish was ...

According to ... disappointed cinema-goers ... She wished that people ...

It's a seven o'clock start for postman W S, six days a week. However, if he ... he would ...

Despite the fact that her colleagues ..., Lee Rin Ne finds that ... When they have moved to their new premises, however, she ....

c Choose two of the people above and write a sentence to say what you would do to improve life if you were in their situations.

Grammar

Would

Here are twelve sentences with <u>would</u>. How many express past habit? How many express hypothesis? What about the others?

a Often there would be a village band made up of self taught players.
b Well, what would you say?
c I feel sure I would be suitable to do the job.
d Some would write their own songs or set new words to tunes they already knew.
e It assured Mrs Bradbrook there would be no further delay.
f I thought you would be interested to hear of the outcome.
g On the way to the shops with her mother she would say 'That's where I used to be a nurse.'
h Being a parent I would certainly have contacted the police.
i The one on the left hand side, I would imagine, is the violin player.
j If I was living near to home I think I would go home and change.
k My brother would say 'Oh, your mother spoils you.'
l I feel a job in an organisation like yours would be likely to lead to future career prospects.

Review

Make adjectives from these nouns. How many can you use in the phrases below? Use a dictionary.

ambition	anger	courage	danger
extinction	peace	profit	ugliness
redundancy	shock	surprise	

Mr Botibol was a/an _____ man.
e.g. *ambitious, courageous*

a His wife would be _____
b Some animal species are now virtually _____
c The building was _____
d The cast were _____ when the play was taken off.
e Nuclear energy for _____ purposes is OK.
f Workers were made _____ to make businesses more _____
g Demonstrations by the union members were far from _____
h Ample measures were taken to keep things _____

> The Grammar Words for this unit are the Wh-words: what, when, where, which, who, why, how etc. See Grammar Book page 60.

Unit 23
Hopes and plans

232 **Trying to diversify**

Words and phrases linking clauses/sentences

Find where these words fit, and write them in.

and	as well as	down which	from there
fact	just generally	that	what (2)

BONNY _____ we're always trying to do is diversify. We started off as a group _____ just sang a few local folk-songs. And _____ we've broadened out to doing things like pantomime. Er, we've written a book. Erm, we do things about Thomas Hardy and his connections with music. _____ , we're hoping to get a book – write a book about that soon, _____ doing a recording. Erm, we do quite a lot of radio work. Television. Erm. I can see –. _____ I would like to do is to be able to write songs for films and plays, _____ Pete and Mac or Roger would write the music. . . . There's all sorts of avenues _____ we can go; _____ broaden our horizons all the time.

Underline words and phrases about the future.

234 **Dip in the pool**

Finish each of these sentences so that they mean the same as the first one.

a   Mr Botibol was both frightened and excited.
    As well as being _____
    _____ .

b   There was only one other person in sight.
    He could _____ .

c   . . . her collar was turned up so Mr Botibol couldn't see her face.
    It was impossible _____
    _____ .

d   The thought of leaping off a ship into the ocean had made Mr Botibol unusually careful.
    Mr Botibol was being _____
    _____ .

e   He was by no means satisfied yet that this women . . .
    He still was not _____
    _____ .

f   All he had to do was check it by talking to her for a moment beforehand.
    He simply had to talk _____
    _____ .

236 **Describe . . .**

Personal qualities

To which job advert do three of these lost paragraphs (A–D) belong? There will be one paragraph left over – which one? _____ . Use a dictionary if you need to.

A
Enthusiasm, liveliness and a capacity for hard work are more important than previous experience.

B
The person we appoint will be a fast accurate typist, able to take responsibility and work with a minimum of supervision. An outgoing, friendly personality and a sense of humour are a must.

C
Ideally you will be a graduate and in your twenties or early thirties with a few years' relevant business experience. You should have good writing and editing skills and above all a creative approach. The ability to communicate clearly and tactfully is essential together with the flexibility to tackle a wide range of Public Affairs tasks.

D
The successful applicant will also be able to work accurately and efficiently under pressure and have an eye for detail. Word processing skills would be an advantage as would language skills.

PUBLICITY CONTROLLERS

Basil Blackwell, the Oxford-based academic publishers, are looking for two people interested in making a career in book marketing. The jobs will involve a wide range of activities helping to promote one of the best lists in publishing, including catalogue preparation, advertising and mailing list research. This is an excellent opportunity for young graduates keen to make a career in marketing books.

LONDON SCHOOL OF HYGIENE AND TROPICAL MEDICINE

ADMINISTRATIVE SECRETARY
PERSONNEL OFFICE

The Personnel Office deals with a wide range of staffing matters at this postgraduate medical school. We need a fourth person to complete a busy team, and to be responsible for the smooth running of the office, provide secretarial support for the Personnel Officer and undertake a variety of administrative and record-keeping tasks.

AU PAIR IN AMERICA

We are looking for an administrative/secretarial assistant to work in our busy Kensington offices.

This post is suitable for a highly motivated person aged 20+ with at least one year's office experience and the following skills:

- Good typing (60 wpm)
- Numeracy
- Good telephone manner

Finally, read through the adverts again. Underline all the words to do with personality, character, and personal abilities.

Circle words to do with work experience and qualifications.

Check any words you think you may need in a dictionary.

 237 **Grammar** ·

Adverbs

Find an adverb from the box that could be used instead of the word or phrase underlined. Which one have you not used.

> awfully apparently deliberately equally greatly increasingly just nevertheless obviously rapidly shortly soon totally

1 I <u>very much</u> appreciate your help, but I must be going <u>shortly</u>.

2 <u>Similarly</u> I would say that ...

3 I consider he was <u>entirely</u> the wrong person to send to Africa. <u>But even so</u>, he enjoyed it.

4 They became <u>more and more</u> exhausted as the day grew hotter.

5 I <u>merely</u> wanted to say how <u>terribly</u> sorry I am about Paul.

6 Did you see that? He's quite <u>clearly</u> destroyed it all <u>on purpose</u>.

7 <u>It is generally said</u> that he used to be a calm child.

240 **Review**

Complete the gaps with the correct preposition.

a How can you reduce the risk _____ falling victim _____ serious crime?
b Is there any chance _____ getting aid there?
c I can't see a different way _____ doing it.
d There was always the risk _____ shooting.
e He would pick it up straight from the ship and drive it home just for the pleasure _____ seeing Ethel's face ...
f 'Tell me', he said, coming straight _____ the point ...
g Yes, that's one way _____ doing it.
h And then he hits on this crazy plan _____ jumping overboard.
i ... making sufficient noise _____ attract attention.
j ... if he was to have any hope _____ winning it now.
k The main precaution is _____ make sure someone sees him going.
l We have had the privilege _____ entertaining guests from Thailand, Ethiopia and Sarawak.

> The Grammar Word for this unit is <u>would</u>.
> See Grammar Book page 61.

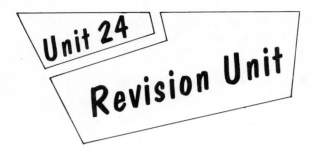

Unit 24
Revision Unit

241 How observant are you?

Which picture is this about?

This could be part of a hurricane lamp which the Webber family talked about in connection with the man-eater leopard incident in Tsavo National Park. Richard Webber thought of using the lamp to scare away the leopard.

Write some short paragraphs similar to the one above explaining four of these pictures. Use the table to help if you wish.

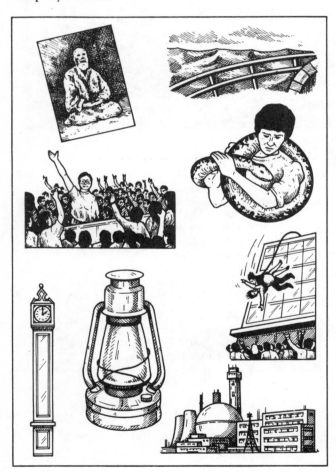

This could be I think this is It looks as though it's This must be	from the part of the a section of the	where which in which after which who whose ___

Language study

Different patterns in text

Situation comment (evaluation)
General specific
Situation problem solution evaluation
A sequence of events/stages
Topic – illustration
Hypothesis – evidence – conclusion

a Which text patterns do these sets of notes follow?

b Use the notes to build up short summaries.

1 More and more/cars/increase/pollution/electric cars/cheaper/ cleaner
2 constant noise/bad ? Scientists report/animals/ noise/unresponsive, violent. Same true/humans?
3 travel/sea/Sealink ferries/pleasant/relaxing/ holiday atmosphere
4 enquire cost, timetable/book in advance/train/car to port./check in 30 mins before sailing time/get on board/relax/enjoy/trip./once arrived/car or other transport/final destination.
5 Older people/talk/childhood./One old lady/village life/games
6 book/published/aim/convince adults/preserve natural environment/limit development. For instance/children/write/urbanisation/polution/ save species
7 concert/given/Yetties/lively/fun/joined in

243 Summarising

Write this summary out again using a more formal written style. You will need to make two kinds of changes:

a Change the verb tenses from present to past narrative.

b Adapt the style, e.g. the sentences may need to be shorter, or structured and punctuated more clearly. A few of the words and phrases marked * are too colloquial to keep in a formal written account. Obviously you would omit the 'erms' and 'ers'!

Erm, after grilling* the purser, he comes to the conclusion that the lowest number possible is going to be the winning one so he's literally going to put his shirt on it* and buy with the winnings his dream car so that erm he can impress his wife when he gets home, erm. He goes to bed after the auction, – he's managed to get the number he wants – and in the morning, to his horror, he finds that the erm the weather has suddenly turned beautiful and the ship is steaming along at a great speed so he's in a real panic then – what can he do? How can he face his wife having gambled all their savings? And then he hits on this crazy plan of jumping overboard so that the ship will have to stop to pick him up.

After discussing the matter in depth with the purser.

After finding out as much as he could from the purser.

After completing your summary, underline two examples of <u>had</u> being used for past perfect, and circle three examples of verb phrases used to express the future in the past.

Grammar revision

Adverbs

Adverbs can be used to modify adjectives.
e.g.
A: I've been on a hovercraft when it's rough.
B: How rough?
A: I've been on a hovercraft when it's <u>fairly</u> rough.

Fill in the missing letters to form adverbs.

c__mpl__t__ly	r____lly	h__ghly
__bs__l__t__ly	__wf__lly	s__rpr__s__ngly
__xtr__m__ly	t__rr__bly	r____s__n__bly
__n__s__lly	dr____df__lly	r__l__t__v__ly
m__d__r__t__ly	__nt__r__ly	sl__ghtly

Adverbs also modify whole clauses or sentences:

<u>Frankly</u>, I do not believe it.
<u>Usually</u> the Mums are right because they are naturally cautious and men have to show off.

Can you work out these words from their phonetic transcriptions?

beɪsɪkə°li'	ɪndiːd	pɜːsə°nəli'
kliəli'	lʌkɪli'	sɛ
kjʊəriəsli'	nætʃrəli'	kəndli'
fɜːstli'	nɔːməli'	səpraɪzɪŋli'
fɔːtʃə⁴nətli'	ɒbviəsli'	ʌnfɔːtʃə⁴nə'tli'
		ʌnlʌkɪli'

D*s*p*e*r*n*e

a Study these words and definitions.

encounter = unexpected meeting
vanished = disappeared suddenly
whisked = moved very quickly

> **UFO, UFOs.** A **UFO** is an object seen in the sky or landing on earth which cannot be identified and which some people believe to be a spaceship from another planet. **UFO** is an abbreviation for 'unidentified flying object'.
>
> **alien, aliens.** 1 **Alien** means **1.1** belonging to a different country, race, or group. EG . . . *a social system which was determined by alien rulers.* **1.2** strange and sometimes frightening, because of not being part of your normal experience. EG . . . *this totally alien and threatening environment.*
> **2** If something is **alien** to your normal feelings, beliefs, or behaviour, it is not the way you would normally feel or behave. EG *Malice towards an enemy was compeltely alien to the man's nature.*
> **3** An **alien** is **3.1** someone who is not a legal citizen of the country in which they live; a legal term. EG *On arrival in the United Kingdom you must report to the Aliens Registration Office.* **3.2** someone who feels that they do not belong to the society in which they live. EG *They felt themselves to be rebels, aliens and exiles rather than heroes.* **3.3** a creature from outer space, especially one that is considered to be threatening or hostile; used mainly in science fiction.
> ► used as an adjective. EG . . . *an alien spacecraft.*

Which meaning of <u>alien</u> is used in this story? _____

> A FRIGHTENED secretary has vanished a day after claiming she had an encounter with aliens.
> Jackie Smith, 39, disappeared leaving her first month's wages from a new job untouched and furniture at a new house unpacked.
> She was reported missing at the weekend two weeks after she vanished, by a distant aunt, her only relative.
> Her boss Andy Egan has hired a UFO investigator to find her.
> Jackie, of Warrington, Cheshire, had arrived at work in a panic after her alleged encounter, he said yesterday.
> She said green men got into her car which was whisked into the air. The next she remembered was waking up and finding blue dots on her ankles.
> Andy, 25, said: "It may sound like a joke but it most certainly isn't. She turned up at the office in a hell of a panic."
> UFO expert Jenny Randles said: "People have been known to experience the same sort of encounter as Jackie.
> "The blue dots are a classic sign of alien presence. Jackie may now be hiding somewhere terrified that they will come back and get her."

b Find three words/phrases that mean <u>say</u>. What three sources are quoted for this story?

c Who is Jackie Smith?
List all you know about Jackie Smith (personal details, background – not about the events in this story). Then write it up in a paragraph.

> e.g. *Jackie Smith comes from... She is single, her only relative being...*

d What exactly happened?
Write three or four sentences giving a brief account in chronological order of what apparently happened to Jackie Smith.

> e.g. *After starting a new job under boss Andy Eagan, Jackie Smith moved her furniture to a new house. One day while driving to work...*

e What do you think could have happened? Write a short paragraph giving your ideas.

249 Letter writing

Imagine you were writing a letter to Bonny Sartin, manager of the Yetties Folk Group, to ask the group to come and give a concert at your language centre. Offer approximate alternative dates, times, describe the venue (the hall/concert room), describe who the audience would be. Enquire about fees, travel etc.

ADDRESS
Mr Bonny Sartin,
The Yetties,
PO Box 3,
Sherborne
Dorset DT9 3AW

Grammar Book

This Grammar Book enables you to revise and consolidate your knowledge of English grammar, and build up a useful reference section. It will also help you improve your reading speed, as you re-read familiar texts and transcripts to find examples. These examples have been carefully selected to illustrate useful patterns in English, and revise vocabulary and idiomatic phrases.

Each unit in the Practice Book has a Grammar Word which appears in this appendix. A short explanation for each category of the word is provided, followed by some examples. You may add an extra example in the space provided. The section references, e.g. (59), (63ts) will help you find these examples, some of which are taken from the written texts in the Student's Book and some from the transcripts of the spoken conversation (marked ts). If a section number is marked x 2, there are two examples in that section. In each case, choose the example you find the most useful. After completing each Grammar Word you may like to refer to the Key, which provides a clue word for each example. The clue words are taken from the sentences in which the examples can be found.

List of entries

	Unit		
a/an	1	it	2
as	3	must	15
at	10	of	8
be	9	on	20
by	16	that	19
can/could	14	the	5
do/does/did	6	to	13
for	17	wh-	22
get	11	will	18
have	7	with	21
if	12	would	23
in	4		

a, an   1

1 one of many EG *I work as an administrator for a small charity*. (2ts) *I don't actually have a job at the moment.* (4) *Thought it was a terrific place.* (10ts)

(10ts x2) ....

2 used instead of the number 'one'. EG *I have two step-sisters and a step-brother.* (4) *I'd like a moment to think about that.* (30ts)

(10ts) ....

3 used in phrases which indicate a quantity or amount EG *Then you relaxed a bit.* (4ts) *a couple of years.* (10ts)

(10ts x 2) ....

as   3
1 specifying a feature or function EG *I work as an administrator for a small charity* (2ts) *I did training as a state enrolled nurse* (17b ts)

(20c, 24) ....

1.1 to show how we regard something or think of it. EG *He did it as a joke.*

(29b ts) ....

2 as . . . – often in comparisons. EG *Trying to get as many recitals as possible* (2ts) *Just as quickly as anyone else.* (234). Sometimes in fast speech the first as is omitted.

(24b ts) ....

2.1 the way something happens or is done; meaning in the same way as, similar to. EG *Folk song was handed on from generation to generation, as were the ceremonial customs and ritual dances.* (20a) *. . . which isn't quite the same thing as telling a lie.* (29b ts)

(17b ts end) ....

3 = when, at the same time. EG *. . . as the singing increased, I didn't seem to have time for my full time job.* (17b)

(31) ....

4 as if, as though, when giving a possible explanation for something. EG *Don't cross your arms and legs, it looks as though you are withholding information.* (31)

(29b ts) ....

5 because. EG *As you've just left school* you would need a reference from a head teacher.

___

6 in phrases, to introduce a comment. EG *As you can see*, it's fairly conventional stuff. (4ts) *As far as the foreign tours are concerned . . .* (27ts)

(17b ts, 24a ts) ___

___

7 other useful phrases with as EG *. . . series* **such as** *'These Musical Islands'.* (20c) *that one* **as well** (24b) *Saying too much* **as well as** *too little.* (29b) **As long as** *I have my rights.* (59)

___

at 10

1 where (which part). EG *at the top* of a mountain. (34ts) *on a sandbank, with his tail hanging over* **at one end** *and his snout in the water* **at the other end** (95)

(24b ts) ___

1.1 in a place thought of in terms of what happens there. EG *You arrive* **at a party.** (59) **at work.**

(102 x2, 14b) ___

2 the time when something happens. EG **At about 7** *Mum's key in the lock* (64) *I don't exaggerate* **at this point** (110b ts). *We noticed* **at one stage** *it had disappeared* (150b ts).

(65) ___

3 look at, shout at, smile at etc. EG **staring at the sea** (234) *She turned and* **smiled at him** (239)

(59, 63ts) ___

___

4 used to answer the questions 'How much/old/fast? EG *the speed* **at which** *a rider is shot clear . . .* (86b) *I left school* **at the age of 18.** (139) *available* **at such a low price** (78)

(72a, 102 part 4) ___

___

5 other useful phrases with at EG *It means nothing to me* **at all.** (90ts) *it resembled, in shape,* **at any rate,** *a . . .* (234). *I wanted to do maths but* **at the same time** *I wanted . . .* (106ts)

(95 x2, 100c ts) ___

___

6 after adjectives like good, bad, surprised, shocked. EG *I'm not very* **good at** *the scientific side of it* (83ts). *I was* **shocked at** *his behaviour.* **I'm surprised at you!**

be (am, is, are, was, were, be, been) 9

1 answering the question 'Who?' or 'What?' – followed by a noun or noun phrase. EG *Maybe* **his father or mother was a biologist.** (90b ts) **They are benign creatures.** *All they want is* **a quiet life.** (91b ts) *The oldest official age recorded* **is that of an American alligator.** (95)

(91, 95) ___

2 answering the question 'What . . . like?' – followed by an adjective. EG **He was too small** *to open the door without using both hands.* (87a) *A wallet can* **be bulky** (78d) **That is rather long,** *isn't it?*

(95, 94) ___

3 describing place where, or situation – often used with a preposition. EG *. . . I missed him when* **he was at school** (56ts) *British scientists believe* **they may be on the verge** *of a major breakthrough.* (83a)

(72c, 91ts) ___

3.1 with 'there', particularly to show location or existence EG **There is a zoo** *down there.* (90b ts) *I mean* **there could be another side** *to the story* (90b ts)

(94b ts, 95) ___

4 to express a continuous action or describe a state, followed by a verb with -ing. EG *But when* **he is driving** *he does the same things himself.* (68) *But while* **the policeman was moving** *Padilla's car off the road . . .* (72) *He was young enough* **to be drinking milk.** (110b ts)

(80 x2, 87a) ___

5 for the passive, followed by a past participle ending in -ed or -en. EG **They were chosen** *from about 31,000 entries.* (45b) **The world population of them has been drastically reduced.** (97) *Stories about* **people being eaten** *by crocodiles* (95)

(95 x4) ___

6 followed by a clause EG *The other thing I felt* **was that letter number two had much more detailed information.** (24ts) *That* **was when they punctured his tyres,** *wasn't it?* (72ts) *The situation* **is that you don't always want . . .** (78ts)

(68c ts, 94b ts) ___

7 expressions with 'I'm . . .'. EG **I'm afraid** *I don't know.* [9] **I'm not sure** *whether they do.* [9] **I'm sorry.**

by 16

1 used after a passive verb to show who/what did it. EG *written by a small child*. (45) *people being attacked by crocodiles* (95) *story told by a rubber planter* (95) *A strike by Madrid underground workers* (154)

(150a, 163a) ....

2 used particularly before a verb with -ing, to answer the question 'How?'. EG *travelling by bus*. (59) *cleanse two reservoirs near Glasgow by frightening away 5000 gulls*. (80ts) *by accident*. (237c) *by telex* (133d)

(38, 113) ....

3 when, before or at a stated time. EG *by then* (133c) *by the end of the evening*. (43ts) *By the time she was ...* (196)

(133a x2, 133e) ....

4 explaining where: next to, close to, going past. EG *stood by his side*. (219) *and as the animal came by, I swished the lamp at it*. (110b ts)

(21, 166b ts) ....

5 to express the amount of increase/decrease. EG *increase the quota of kangaroos by half a million*. (150)

(154, 166c ts) ....

6 with 'mean'. EG *I wonder what they mean by a big ship?* (204ts) *What do you mean by ...?*

(94b ts) ....

7 in phrases such as **by the way, by no means**. EG *You are at a – there are only three more, by the way, – you are at a small dinner party ...* (59ts) *He was by no means satisfied yet* (234a) *take the future day by day* (232c ts)

can, could 14

1 used to show that something is possible, that someone is able to do something EG *News can be something people want you to know or it can be something people want to hide*. (143) *Nobody could find this flight-case. It could have been in any one of six or seven capitals*. (100)

(140a x2, 143c x2) ....

1.1 could for suggestions. EG *You could read more widely. Couldn't you borrow a dictionary?*

(106a ts) ....

2 used to ask for or give permission. EG *You can go now. Could I come tomorrow instead of today?*

3 used to make an offer or request. EG *Can I help you? Could you pass on that message* (76c) *I said "Can we have some food?"* (45b)

(133d x2) ....

4 with words like 'see', 'hear', 'remember' etc. EG *Can you believe it?* (116ts) *Maybe it could smell us*. (109c) *I can't see why it isn't possible*. (201b)

(109, 116 ts) ....

NOTES: In categories 1 and 4 **could** is the past tense form of **can**. In categories 1.1, 2 and 3 **could** is generally regarded as a more formally polite form than **can**.

could is also preferred to **can** to show some doubt about the truth or likelihood of what is stated. EG *There might, I mean there could be another side to the story*. (90b ts)

do (does, doing, done, did) 6

1 used to form questions. EG *Do you actually have an agent yourselves?* (27ts) *How long does it take to learn?* (17a) *Did he ever feel he was never going to get out?* (40ts)

(59a 59b) ....

2 used to make a verb negative. EG *I don't actually have a job at the moment*. (4) *So you didn't suddenly join the group*. (17b ts)

(59a ts x3) ....

2.1 Don't or do not used when telling people not to do something. EG *Don't smoke*. (31) *Don't cross your arms or legs*. (31)

(31 x3) ....

3 used to stand for and refer back to an earlier verb EG *Monkey did not say yes as he should do*. (45b) *Do they have crocodiles in Egypt? I'm not sure they do*. (94ts)

(25a, 45b) ....

4 used with a noun to show an activity EG *I've just done two concerts in the North*. (2) *I did a five-year apprenticeship*. (17a ts) *What travelling have you done?* (17b ts)

(56a) ....

5 as a general word for activity or for someone's work: EG *What did you do before you became a full-time musician?* (17a ts) *I don't think I'd do any of those.* (59a ts)

(2ts, 64)

6 for emphasis EG *But actually I did go up in a plane the other day.* (47ts) *Do sit still.* (31)

(31, 27ts)

6.1 as a very polite invitation or request EG *I do hope you will be able to come round some time.* (48) *Do forgive me for butting in.* (62) *Do sit down.*

for 17

1 used to show who wants or needs something, or who benefits . . . EG (93) *at a School for the Blind. efficient support for the Yetties.* (123) *a song for all of mankind.* (123)

(172b ts, 176b)

2 used to answer the questions 'Why?' or 'What for?':

2.1 to indicate reason or purpose. EG *Hospital sources say she has been admitted for medical checks.* (161c) *Many thanks for your help* (133a) *no further permission would be given for building on farmland* (163b ts) *All for the love of Selina.* (176) *for economic reasons* (173)

(176 ts, 176)

2.2 to introduce information about purpose after certain nouns, adjectives, verbs, such as 'arrangements/enquiry' 'good/bad', 'look/search/ask/apply for'. EG *ask XAL for an explanation and an apology for this.* (133f) *A bad start to the tour for the Yetties* (133f)

(102, 176c ts x2)

3 to introduce expressions of time and distance.

3.1 to answer the questions 'How long?' and 'How far?' EG *kept in Nairobi for some time.* (114 ts) *For several days.* (185a) *You can drive for miles.*

(137 ts x2, 172)

3.2 to show when something must be completed. EG *Can you read this for tomorrow?*

4 meaning 'because' EG *. . . in a kind of shocked surprise. For it was at this moment the idea came.* (229a)

get, got 11

1 to move somewhere to reach a place, usually followed by a preposition. EG *got out of bed* (109ts) *get on the bus.* (59) *got off the plane* (100ts) *Mrs Kerr got home.* (102)

(104 x2, 110b/c ts x2)

2 have got = to possess or have with you. (Compare 'have' 1.1). EG *We've got a photo here.* (13ts) *Have you got any others?* (29ts)

(45)

3 have got to for obligation or necessity. (Compare 'have' 4). EG *What we've got to decide is whether . . .* (80c)

(72b ts)

4 to obtain/receive/take EG *you don't get the job.* (29b ts) *Why have I got a new cooker?* (102ts)

(110c ts)

5 to turn/become/grow. EG *as your parents get a bit richer.* (63ts) *He got very depressed.* (49ts) *people are getting used to the idea* (49ts) *If this gets any worse . . .* (210)

(110c ts, 114ts x2)

6 to cause someone to do something, or to cause something to be in a particular place. EG *trying to get the Germans to buy British goods.* (137ts) *I got John in the car.* (216ts) *They put it on a Thai Airlines flight and got it back to Nepal.* (100d ts)

(95, 100c ts)

7 instead of be to form passives EG *someone who sells stories and gets paid by the piece.* (140b ts) *Would he get caught . . .?* (239) *all of us got married after we turned professional.* (216 ts)

8 to do something (eventually) after a delay EG *song . . . on the radio, therefore the public get to hear it.* (130ts) *By the time I get to drive a car . . .* (223)

have (has, having, had) 7

1.1 to own or possess EG *She has this little summer-house.* (4ts) *The gypsy had no castle or money.* (21)

(56a ts)

1.2 be related to EG *I have a little nephew.* (48)

(63ts)

2 showing where something is. EG *Say **you have something stuck in a tooth**.* (59a) (= There is something stuck in your tooth.) *It **always has lumps** when it's in school dinners.* (53ts) (= there are always lumps in it . . .) *Each **village had its singers, storytellers and musicians**.* (14)

(72a, 72c) ....

3 with expressions of time EG *I **had a year** in Vannes.* (10ts) *I didn't **have time** to finish this.*

(64) ....

4 have to for necessity or obligation (see **get** 3) EG *Last one to bed **has to switch off** the lights.* (34) *I **had to take** a couple of years off.* (32b ts)

(69c ts, 69b) ....

5 sometimes **have** does not have any real meaning itself – it takes its meaning from the words that come after it.

5.1 EG ***Have** you any plans to go abroad?* (10ts) *Let's **have a look** around the country.* (17a ts)

(83c ts, 19) ....

5.2 with food and drink EG *Have you **had dinner** yet? Shall we **have some coffee?/a coffee break?***

(53) ....

5.3 especially of things in the mind EG: ***Have a clear idea** of the subjects you wish to take* (31 ts) *He might **have a point*** (76b)

(34 ts, 47 ts) ....

6 used to make the present perfect tense (have + -ed/-en)

6.1 when we are talking about the past but thinking about the present. EG *I've **also visited** Greece and Spain on holiday.* (10ts) *I've **just jumped** off the Empire State Building.* (36) *He's **had** a really amazing life.* (91b ts)

(20b, 56a ts) ....

6.2 for something that will have happened at some time in the future. EG *Answer the questions **after you have read** the passage. Please will you get in touch **as soon as you have received** the tickets?*

7 had for the past perfect tense EG *When I realised . . . and began shouting, the staff **had all gone** home.* (38b) *Go in as if nothing **had happened**.* (59)

(38b, 72) ....

8 have after may, might, can, could, etc. When talking about the past. EG *I **must have been** about eleven or twelve* (17a ts) *I **may have blocked** it out of my memory.* (34ts)

(72b ts x3) ....

9 had = if. EG ***Had you come** earlier, you could have got tickets* (= If you had come). ***Had I known**, I would have got there at 8am* (= If I had known . . .)

if 12
1 in conditions.

1.1 when the speaker thinks something is likely to happen or to have happened. EG *Include your phone number **if you have one**.* (25) ***If I have had** a bad experience, I may have blocked it out.* (34ts) ***If I go up** a ladder I'm scared stiff now.* (34ts) *I'll fly **if ever I can**, now.* (204 ts)

(34, 121a ts) ....

1.2 for something the speaker imagines, or believes is unlikely or not real. EG ***If an adult had written it**, it would have sounded a lot more dull* (45ts) ***If you were travelling by bus** and only had a £20 note, would you walk home?* (59) ***If I'd gone away** for 9 months I think I would've had a much better time.* (106a)

(45c, 49ts) ....

2 if/whether in indirect questions, after 'know, ask, see, find out, remember' etc. EG ***See if** they want the crocodiles kept.* (97ts) ***If you wanted** to find out whether someone was an optimist . . .* (62) *Let me know by telex **if any flights are impossible**.* (133)

(71 x2, 80c ts) ....

3 as if/as though. EG *It looks **as if** you're interested.* (31ts)

(31, 59) ....

4 in polite requests. EG ***If you can just sign** that for me . . . thank you. **If you wouldn't mind waiting** a moment, I'll be with you. I would be grateful **if you would ask** XAL for an explanation . . .* (133)

5 Other phrases with **if**: if only, even if, if ever, if you like, what if . . ., if any, if not, if so. EG ***If only** I'd had the advantages you've had.* (215b) *What you come back to is, **if you like**, the basic skill of journalism.* (143d ts) ***What if** he can't get to the scene . . .?* (143c)

(68c ts, 72a) ....

in 4

1 expressing where: in or into a place. EG *in South Europe* (10) *in the London area* (27ts); *in Bristol*; (24) *lived in the villages* (32b ts); *water in a pipe* (34b); *after being locked in* (38b).

(36x3, 38x3) ....

1.1 for books, pictures, newspapers etc. EG *In the original song* (21). *In letter two* ... (24a ts)

(24) ....

2 for groups of people. EG *In its small isolated communities* (2); *students in your group* (32c)

(17a ts, 27ts) ....

3 when, during eg *in the evenings* (2); *in 1967* (13); *here, in their early years* (20c); *in the course of the last few years* (29b ts)

(17a ts, 34) ....

3.1 after a length of time eg *In a week's time.*

4 how something is expressed, in what way/manner/terms EG *much in the manner of* the village bands of days gone by (20c) *Thinking in terms of what you were saying* (25ts) *State your qualifications in brief* (25b). *Apply in writing. In French. Sit there in absolute silence.* (29b)

(24tsx2, 31 x2) ....

5 in a particular situation. *in the interview* (29ts) *in an awkward situation.* (68ts)

(16, 24) ....

6 Wearing, dressed in. EG *the lady in the red dress.* (13ts) *the fellow in glasses.*

7 in an emotional state EG *In embarrassment. In her excitement* ... *Seagulls in distress.* (80) *Look back in anger.*

8 Other phrases: *with the same firm, in fact* (17a ts) *Work ... was getting in the way of singing* (17a ts) *a certain worry, but only in as much as I'd finished my apprenticeship and* ... (17a ts) *In view of my qualifications* (24)

it 2

1 referring back:

1.1 to something specific, already mentioned or known by both speakers. EG *That (photograph) looks like you, doesn't it?* (4ts) ... *I like the (bush with) yellow flowers. I don't know what it's called.* (4ts)

(4ts x5) ....

1.2 to a more general situation. EG *It was so cheap it was unbelievable.* (referring to life in Spain) (10ts) *How did it happen?* (Roger's joining the Yetties group.) (17b ts)

(4, 17b ts) ....

2 referring forward to something or someone specific, or a general situation. EG *I found it more interesting to walk about.* (10ts) *It was nice seeing you.* (239)

(2) ....

2.1 often followed by a 'who' or 'that' clause EG *I think it's the third one on the right that comes next.* (176)

(10ts, 13ts) ....

3 referring to the general situation (including time, weather) EG *It's noisy here. It was dark. It's about 7pm. It was bitterly cold.* (38)

(4ts end) ....

4 for an unknown person EG *Who was it on the phone? Sometimes it's just anybody; sometimes it's a particular person.* (154)

must 15

1 necessity or obligation EG *You must come to an agreement about each one.* (94a) *Marcos must go.* (184a)

(143c ts) ....

2 to show that you have good reason to believe something eg *The next one must be summer.* (124ts) *I tend to think they must be there for a reason.* (97ts) *This must be winter.* (124ts) *Must be, mustn't it?* (15ts)

2.1 followed by **have** for past tense EG *I think they must have got them mixed up.* (113) *They must have left the car engine on.* (72ts)

(116ts, 94b ts) ....

3 for a very polite offer or suggestion EG *You must come and visit us some time.*

(48) ....

4 in phrases like **I must admit, I must say.** EG *I used to spend hours, I must admit, walking around* ... (10ts)

(10ts) ....

1.1 used in expressions of quantity, size, amount, such as: a lot of, a number of, one of, quite a bit of, plenty of. EG *any of the others.* (45d ts) ***the bulk of** what they're trying to get across* . . . (80c ts) *a fire caused £500,000 **worth of** damage.* (166 ts)

(87b x2) ....

1.2 containing/consisting of something. EG *a cup of tea. a panel of judges* (45b) *a pair of socks.*

(87a) ....

1.3 to express 'part of' a whole. EG *in the middle of the road* (72). *steering wheels of some cars.* (87b) *the scientific side of it.* (83c ts) *member of the family* (63ts)

(87a, 87b) ....

2.1 belonging to EG *the offices **of** the television station* (36)

(25b x2, 36) ....

2.2 concerning, relating to, about. EG (38ts) *methods of escape.* (61) *the effects of being a middle child.* (63) *talking in terms of space and articles.* (76ts) *Ministry of the Environment.* (112)

(47ts x2) ....

3 sort of, type of etc

3.1 **sort of** spoken only – used to show the speaker does not want to be exact; or instead of a pause or hesitation. EG *That was **what sort of** age?* (32b ts) *You need **sort of** snappy judgement really.* (68ts) *It has **a sort of** breaking effect.* (83ts)

(45ts x2, 76ts) ....

3.2 **sort of, type/kind/form/version of** etc EG *this sort of childlike style* (45d ts) *another type of dole scheme.* (49ts)

(21, 43 x2) ....

4 used with dates, times, ages, sizes, scores EG *at the beginning of the 20th Century.* (21) *at the age of three.* (43) *a total audience of 1700 or so* (100)

(74) ....

5 after nouns that have been formed from verbs such as hope, fear, love, memory etc. EG *I have some sort of irrational **fear of** ghosts.* (34ts) *their obvious **love of** their native Dorset.* (20)

(34ts) ....

1 place

1.1 where something/someone is. EG *on the factory floor.* (14) *I've been **on a hovercraft.*** (204ts) . . . *so it stood ninety years **on the floor.*** (219)

(150a ts x2, 184b) ....

1.2 where you go or where something is put. EG *on coach outings* (14b) *The waiter sprinkled water **on the tablecloth.*** (207a) . . . *the stuff that's been spilt **on the table.*** (207b ts)

(110b ts, 210b) ....

1.3 in phrases. EG *On the right/left hand-side.* (13ts) *On the banks of a river.* (95) *On stage.* (100ts) *On the next page.* (90c) *on the top of the door.* (110c ts) *On the way to the shops* (198c)

2 time. EG *At football matches **on Saturday afternoons.*** (14b) *published **on April Fool's Day.*** (201a) ***On one occasion** a lion killed 71 goats* (114)

(14b x2, 24) ....

3 about or concerning. EG *Advice to women **on how to reduce** the risk of falling victim to violence.* (150) *Decide **on the best course** of action.* (176ts) *a listener who had heard earlier reports **on the subject.*** (161d ts)

(133e x2, 201) ....

4 with a journey or holiday. EG . . . *100 people **on a holiday trip** down the Malili river* (95) *Did you have any problems **on the German tour?*** (137ts)

(10ts, 204a ts) ....

5 on radio, television, the telephone, etc. EG . . . *on TV advertisements* and *on Top of the Pops.*

(130b ts x2, 27ts) ....

6 after verbs

6.1 meaning to continue, such as 'go on', 'carry on', 'fight on' etc. EG *It may have **lived on** until 1945.* (95) *they were due to **move on*** (133f) *Okay. Let's **get on** and finish this.*

(184) ....

6.2 with other verbs, such as **depend on, go on** = happen, EG *depends on what you mean by refuse.* (94ts) *checking up on what's going on* (201c ts1)

7 meaning 'when' or 'after' with verbs in -ing or with nouns like 'arrival' or 'departure' formed from verbs. EG *The court clerk accepted the money* **on a promise** *that the remainder . . .* (104) **On hearing** *this from the purser Mr. Botibol decided on the low field.*

(133f) ....

....

8 useful phrases with on: *I'll do it* **on the basis of intelligence.** (172a ts) **on the grounds that** *she's still in shock.* (188a ts) **and so on** (166b ts) **on the way** (198)

that 19

1 referring back (compare it category 1). EG *I do* **agree with that.** (187b ts) *Does he say that people* **do that** *the whole time?* (187a ts) *I think we must use* **things like that** *the whole time without thinking about them.* (187b ts)

(201b ts x3) ....

....

1.1 referring back to the content of an earlier part of the text EG *. . . caution . . . I think* **that's why** *women drivers have been had up in the past.* (68c) *Yes,* **that's right.** (68c)

(176) ....

....

2 used as an adjective, meaning that particular person/thing/time/place etc. EG *At eight o'clock* **that night** *the main dining-room was filled with people.* (206) **At that point** *Mr. Botibol stood up.* (210)

(187a 187b ts) ....

....

3 after certain verbs, adjectives and nouns, to express what is said, thought and felt.

3.1 after verbs like 'say', 'think', 'find'. EG *I feel that they owe us some sort of explanation.* (133f) *I can't believe that it would be displayed to the public.* (201b ts) *I think that that is a genuine story.* (201b ts)

(198a, 200) ....

3.2 after adjectives like 'sure', 'sorry', 'possible', 'likely' etc.: *I'm sure that he wouldn't actually fall to the ground.* (201b ts) *I'd have thought it'd be far more likely that it would be sort of via a university.* (201b ts)

(109, 201b ts) ....

3.3 after nouns like 'fact', 'promise', 'thing' etc. EG *I'll go for the fact that there aren't any crocodiles in Egypt.* (94 ts) *Due to scientific concern that exposure to the light could weaken the already fading image . . .* (200)

(104, 133f x2) ....

4 expressing purpose/result:

4.1 so that EG *Make sure her collar's not turned up* **so that she can't see anything.** (234b ts)

4.2 in a clause after so. EG *Luckily she was* **so surprised** *that she did not try to pull herself from my grasp.* (195)

5 defining things, people etc. EG *Listen to the questions* **that Bob was asked.** (163c) *Note down any new facts and information* **that has not been given** *earlier.* (188)

(201c ts x2) ....

....

the 5

1 The definite article is used when you know which one/s the speaker or writer means because:

1.1 they tell you which one, either before or after. EG **the walls of a local railway station tunnel.** (43) **the bit where she finds the monkey.** (45d ts) **the next day.** (45d ts)

(36 x6) ....

....

1.2 there is only one. EG *in the sun.* (91) *The Bristol Post.* (24) *frightened of the dark.* (34)

(34,36,43) ....

....

1.3 there is only one, or one group of something, around, so it's obvious which one is meant. EG *the government.* (32b ts) *sleep with the light on.* (34ts) *. . . in our garden, watching the trees . . .* (43)

(34ts x6) ....

....

2 instead of a possessive like 'my, our, their'. EG *I was in the car.* (45)

(43) ....

3 referring to a whole but specific group of people or things referred to by an adjective. EG **the rich** *should give more to* **the poor.**

NOTE: You do NOT need the when you are referring to things or people in general. EG *One of the things I really hate is* **spiders and insects.** (34ts) (Which spiders? All spiders; insects in general.) *the trees making* **patterns** *against the sky.* (43) (Which patterns? I don't know – any patterns, all sorts of patterns.) *the way* **men** *drive* (68ts) (which men? men in general.) A basic rule is if you cannot answer the question 'which —?', you don't need 'the'.

to 13

1 with expressions of place, answering the question 'where to?'. EG *You've been* **to Africa.** (10ts) *The Yetties' trip* **to South-east Asia** (133) *One or two of the schools we've been* **to.** (13ts) *your last trip* **to Germany.** (137ts)

(135, 133a) ....

2 answering the question 'who to?' after verbs like give, offer, write, send etc. EG *The man-eater was sent to me in Tsavo.* (112) *I have written to the director.* (112)

(135 x2) ....

....

3 after verbs like 'listen', 'say', 'speak', 'write' etc. EG *You have little self-confidence and wouldn't say boo to a goose.* (65) *So we had a German this end speaking to an English (person) the other end.* (137ts)

(124a, 137ts) ....

....

4 to express purpose, answering the question 'why?'. EG *Grimble started a HOME TOAST DELIVERY SERVICE to earn some extra pocket money.* (48) *So I got out of bed and went to look at the animal.* (109c ts) *all dance and sing to make the crops grow.* (130b ts)

(131ts, 87) ....

....

5 after 'ask', 'like', 'tell', 'want', 'plan', 'start', 'try' etc. for an action EG *He started to leave.* (87) *I asked my wife to get the key.* (110c ts) *I told her to walk, so we walked slowly to another Banda.* (110c ts)

(131ts, 133e) ....

....

6 after verbs like 'have to', 'got to', 'used to', 'going to' EG *My sister used to say the same thing.* (63) *You have to sing outside the store.* (137)

(110b ts, 114ts) ....

....

7 with certain adjectives, often after 'it' EG *It's hard to know quite how it works.* (83ts) *Would it be possible to have the details of the records by then?* (133c) *It's so nice to have breakfast in bed.* (239)

(133a, 133e) ....

....

8 after nouns like 'way', 'thing', 'place', 'problem', 'solution', 'opportunity' etc. EG *... a cheap way to cut down seagulls in the area.* (80) *The solution is to have a slimline wallet.* (78) *Give people the opportunity to join in.* (130b ts)

(85 x2) ....

....

9 from ... to ... EG *able to charm anything from warts to rats* (21) *from generation to generation* (20a)

(20a, 114ts) ....

....

wh- words 22

1 when, where, which, who in defining clauses. EG *the person who gets the correct mile number presumably gets the kitty.* (221 ts) *These are the events which make the headlines.* (183) *There's countries all over the world where they need volunteer health workers.* (226ts)

(223a x2) ....

....

....

2 when in time clauses. EG *My wife gets into a routine when I'm away like that.* (216ts) *But it stopped short, never to go again, when the old man died.* (219)

(226ts, 228b) ....

....

....

3 how, what, when, where, which, who, why:

3.1 after 'tell', 'know', 'ask', 'say', 'remember', 'sure', 'certain', 'reason' etc. EG *State where you saw the job advertised.* (25b) *I can't see why it isn't possible.* (201ts) *I'm not sure what the range is yet.* (210a) *There are two possible reasons why she might fail him.* (234a)

(217b ts2, 224a) ....

....

3.2 In direct questions EG *Where did you live?* (2ts) *Why is Mr. Botibol so concerned about the weather?* (210b) *When do you think the story was written?* (217b ts2)

(228c, 229b x2) ....

....

4 when, where, which, who to introduce describing clauses which refer back to:

4.1 the general or whole situation. EG *... jazz, and would like to ... somehow get that into the curriculum which is quite an ambition ...* (226ts)

(226ts) ....

....

4.2 a specific person/thing/place etc. EG *I've discovered ... from my son who is taking a course in energy, that it's just not needed at all.* (226ts) *He spent most of his life in Dorset, where his novels are set* (232)

(210a) ....

....

5 in clauses after be. EG *This is why I get muddled between alligators and crocodiles.* (94ts) *It had previously killed a little girl. Which is why it had been rounded up.* (114ts)

(172b, 198b) ....

will 18

1 for fact or prediction. EG *The wife* **will get smarter** *if her husband is smart.* (173) *Perhaps a later programme* **will try to interview** *that water expert* (163c ts)

(188a ts x2)

2 to express willingness: to make an offer or announce a decision, intention or promise. EG *OK* **I'll read mine out.** (29b ts) *I'm seeing the Yetties this evening and* **will point out** *that you need the vaccination certificates.* (133a). **We'll simply reverse the film**, *run it through backwards.* (118)

(172b x2)

2.1 to make a request, to ask if someone is willing to do something. EG **Will you start? Will you try** *to come early if you can, please? OK,* **who'll start?**

3 as an alternative to the present simple to express state or habit. EG *Crocodiles* **will eat** *refuse as well as living creatures.* (94) *This slim leather wallet* **will hold** *credit cards and notes.* (78)

(95, 114ts)

with 21

1 together with. EG *I've had lunch* **with them** ... (178) *I'm alone* **with a small baby** (196) *the defeated president left and* **together with thousands of ordinary citizens,** *the world's press* ... (184c ts)

(200, 215)

2 used to describe things or people, and the manner in which they do things. EG *In the front here,* **with long hair and ear-rings,** *is Sarah Jane.* (4ts) **songs with hand actions.** (130ts) *He glanced around* **with approval.** (207a)

(34ts x2, 206 x2)

3 how, using what. EG *beat the leopard off him* **with a lead pipe.** (116ts) *travellers cheques* **with which** *to pay their hotel bills.* (133d)

(217 x2, 217b ts)

4 to express a reason or cause. EG *everything is* **white with snow.** (124) **With more than 8,000 Vietnamese still in Hong Kong's closed camps,** *the Home Office is coming under pressure to* ... (150)

(38, 206)

5 after certain verbs and nouns: agree, compare, involved, argue, continue, to do with, connected etc. EG *never won an* **argument with him.** (187ts)

(207, 210c ts1)

would 23

1 For facts, predictions, decisions, intentions, promises in the past, often when they are being reported. (See **will 1** and **2**) EG *It had assured Mrs. Kerr that her old cooker* **would be returned pronto.** (102) *£220 – this ticket* **wouldn't fetch more than that.** (221b) *It was a question now only of whether the ship* **would be delayed long enough.** (239c)

(45a, 229b)

2 For something which is hypothetical rather than true. EG *What* **would you do if you were Mr. Botibol?** (228c). *This report* **would best be understood by a listener who had heard an earlier report.** (161d ts)

(210a)

3 For habitual actions in the past EG *Often* **there would be** *a village band made up of self taught players.* (20) *People would gather round us and they* **would join in.** (137ts).

(32b x2, 198)

4 as a polite form for requests and offers. EG **Would you mind** *waiting a moment?* **I'd like** *a moment to think about that.* (29b) **Would you like** *a drink?*

(53, 243a ts)

5 in the phrase **would like to** meaning 'want to' EG *I'd like to go and work in a third world country.* (238ts) *What I* **would like to** *do is* ... (232a ts)

(232b ts x3)

6 As a polite form with words like 'say', 'think', 'imagine' etc, sometimes instead of 'do' in questions. EG *Beautiful I would think.* (239a ts) *Would you agree?*

(239a ts, 207b ts)

Key

3 **a**
–, the, the, a, a, –, the, the, a, the, –

4 **b**
brother, older sisters, younger, red hair, Sarah-Jane

12 a in b of c at, at d into, with, of e in f on, of

13 up to, during, in, in, around, from of, for, since, beyond, all over, to, on, in

15 1f 2c 3a 4g 5d 6e 7j 8i
9k 10h 11b

17 **a**
1 the show 2 the Scouts 3 an event 4 problems 5 life in general
b had, had, had, would
c you see, well, you know, and everything

20 1e 2d 3a 4b 5c 6h 7g 8f

23 **d**
1 freedom 2 rural 3 an instrument 4 a boss 5 a chap
6 some drama 7 mental 8 wealthy
9 a president 10 firmly 11 satisfied

26 **a**
a u,c b c,u c u,c d u,c e u,c
f u,c g u,c h u,c i u,c j c,u
k u,c
b
1 help 2 advice 3 energy
4 accommodation 5 control
6 music 7 laughter 8 respect
9 management 10 machinery
11 news

27 a advertisement b qualifications
c management d trainee
e increasingly f assistant
g readable h reference i effective

28 a to b through, up to, at c to
d up, into

29 a Avoid sounding . . .
b Do include the name of the person you are writing to if you know it.
c In view of my qualifications/the fact that I am well qualified, he said . . .
d It was her parents who pushed her to go . . .
e Unless you are suitably qualified, you should not . . .
f Make the information you give relevant to . . .
g Include your telephone number if you have one.
h Don't give an employer the impression you are unlikely to . . .
i A magazine produced by the Midland Bank which gave ten golden rules.
j Begin by writing a rough draft . . .

32 g, f, a, i, d, c, b, e, h

34 **a**
1 after 'all over the world'
2 after 'progressively worse'
3 after 'well established'
4 after 'himself to fly'

37 Without objects: 1a, 2a, 3b, 4a, 5a, 6a, 7b, 8b, 9b, 10b
Objects: 1b rubbish, 2b work, 3a term, 4b trip, 5b advice, 6b football, 7a car, 8a guns, 9a pages, 10a gas

39 1 For some women going to the supermarket makes them feel terrified/is terrifying
2 John's fear of flying was so great that . . .
3 You are responsible for keeping . . .
4 Instead of moving it immediately, you . . .
5 As a result of a breakdown we were . . .
6 On reaching his hotel he phoned home.
7 In spite of taking up to ten tranquillisers a day, he still . . .
8 At first I thought it was someone playing . . .
9 He had been warned of the possibility of the door closing suddenly.
10 Realising that he might die, he ran . . .

41 ordeal, irritable, dump, syndrome, agoraphobia, afflict

44 a Some artists, like Suzanne Juta, . . . others, for instance Henri Matisse, . . .
b Before that, despite the fact that law bored him, he had been working as a clerk in a law office, intending eventually to go into his father's grain business.
Although Matisse was influenced by artists such as Gaugin, the French Impressionist, and Van Gogh, well known for his Sunflowers, it was Cezanne whose work really inspired him.
Ironically, it was Van Gogh who said 'I live in order to paint', but who died taking his own life at the age of 37, unable to sell his paintings and make a living out of them.

55 special, nervous, irritable, tall, dark-haired, worried, interesting

59 **b**
enthusiastic, creative, decent, practical, nasty, reasonable
c
careless, creative/imaginative, elegant, handsome, beautiful, nasty/unpleasant

66 a depression b quite strange, how difficult! c independence
d complaint, contrast

67 a 9 b 7 c 3 d 1 e 8 f 6
g 4 h 2 i 5

68 a after 'for kids', b after 'to blame', c after 'lighter' or at end

70 dawdle, adjust, boredom, tempted, courteous, congested

71 **a**
1 carelessness 2 difference
3 caution 4 supporter
5 judgement 6 comparisons
7 helpless 8 loosen 9 racial
10 capability 11 tighten
b
3, 1, 2, 6, 5, 4

72 1 I stopped a man for drunken driving and speeding the other day.
2 I got him out of the car, handcuffed him and put him in the front passenger seat of the police car.
3 Then, while I was moving his car off the road, I heard my car start up.
4 I looked round and saw him driving off in the wrong direction down the motorway.
5 I jumped in his car and chased after him.
6 He not only kept driving, he speeded up to about 160 kph.
7 I called for help on my radio.
8 The motorway was cleared and a roadblock was set up.
9 I thought that would stop him but it didn't.
10 He smashed right through it.
11 Eventually the only way we could stop him was by putting something on the road to puncture his tyres.
12 Even then he kept going for another three kilometres before finally swerving into a ditch.
13 When we got to him we found he was still handcuffed.
14 I don't know how he did it.
15 Maybe he sat sideways so he was able to use his hands or perhaps he steered with his knees.
16 I asked him and he just laughed.
17 I really would love to know how he did it.

75 1 It is not always a good thing to be cautious.
2 Even though my dad's always putting lots of money into parking meters, he never . . .
3 Once you get nervous you tend to . . .
4 Signal your intentions to pull out.
5 If the road is not clear, don't move off.
6 You don't need to move your head to (be able to) see what is behind you.
7 Driving slowly is not always a good thing.
8 Make sure the road is clear by looking . . .

76 1 gave 2 gave 3 give 4 gave
5 gave 6 gave 7 given 8 give
9 gave 10 gives 11 gave 12 give

79 2,1,3 1,5,2,4,3 3,1,5,2,6,4

88 **a**
motor, motorist, motorway
intend, intention, intentionally
judge, judgement
expect, expected, unexpected, unexpectedly
capable, capably, capability
entertain, entertaining, entertainment
satisfy, satisfied, dissatisfied, satisfaction, dissatisfaction
improve, improved, improving, improvement
observe, observant, observation

b
safe, unsafe, safety
free, freedom
race, racial, racially
dark, darkness
wide, width
long, length
high, height
broad, breadth
busy, business

91 rodents, pets, altitudes, fur, follicle, parasites, penetrating

92 **a**
1 It is an interesting place to walk around
2 I was finding it very difficult
3 How long does it take to learn?
4 I tried to kick the door open but it was no good
5 It was bitterly cold and I realised I might die
6 It would be very nice for me to have a picture that I could keep
7 Is it possible to drive a car with hands tied behind your back?
8 It's alligators they have as pets, isn't it?
9 I think it was a good day for me
10 It stops the person from going over the handlebars

92 **b**
a The colder it got, the faster he began to walk.
b The more you get to know crocodiles, the more you will like them.
c The closer the snake got, the more frightened I became.
d The more you read, the more you learn.
e The older they get, the wiser they become.
f The more you earn, the more you spend.
g The more I tried to calm him down, the angrier he became.

95 a breed b captivity c demand
d prize e survival f traps
g unsuccessful

103 1 misbehaves 2 misjudge
3 misdirect 4 misinformed
5 misrepresent 6 mistrust
7 misrule 8 misfires

105 **b**
1c 2d 3b 4a 5f 6e

106 1 . . . she had called the police
2 . . . she hadn't given the men her carpets
3 . . . she had given clearer instructions.
4 . . . he had listened more carefully
5 . . . he had checked the number
6 . . . she had been at home.

107 1 In spite of feeling very worried, Mrs Moore . . .
2 Despite her suspicions, she gave the men her own carpets.
3 In spite of losing their instrument case, the Yetties still . . .
4 Their case was finally returned safely in spite of being taken . . .
5 Despite the fact that his case was about to be called, Joe . . .

108 **a**
1 unfortunately 2 inconvenience
3 apology 4 nervous
5 replacements 6 misheard
7 arrangements 8 originally
9 reconditioned 10 residence
11 unexpected 12 misfortune
b
a tiny b appliance c cheerful
d meanwhile e judged
f unfortunately g considerable

111 1d 2a 3h 4e 5b 6i 7f 8c
9j 10g

115 **a**
Past time: 2,4
c
1b 2d 3c 4a

117 **a**
1 I had a very frightening experience when I was living in West Africa.
2 I had been told that snakes were very common in that part of the world and that many of them were poisonous.
3 In fact it was particularly dangerous walking late at night when you could stand on a snake without even seeing it.
4 Because of this I was advised to take a torch with me whenever I went out after dark.
5 I remembered this advice as I was walking back to my house one very dark night.
6 I had no torch and it was too dark to see anything on the path in front of me.
7 I began to imagine that there were snakes in the shadows and that I could see them everywhere.

8 Suddenly I stood on something round lying in the path.
9 There was a rustle of leaves and something hit me on the back of the leg.
10 I jumped in the air and screamed out loud.
11 I knew that I had been bitten by a poisonous snake.

117 b
apply, appliance, application, applicant
behave, misbehave, behaviour
connect, disconnect, connection
construct, construction, constructive
convenient, inconvenient, convenience, inconvenience
fortune, misfortune, fortunate, unfortunate
lucky, unlucky, luckily, unluckily
nationalism, nationalist, nationality
person, personal, personally

electric, electrical, electricity
favour, favourite
nation, national, international
reluctant, reluctance
resident, residence
threat, threaten

118
1 There was a famous film director who was planning . . .
2 The sun was supposed to rise slowly out of the ocean as . . .
3 The usual thing is to film the sunrise separately and then throw it . . .
4 The whole scene is filmed with the actors performing in front of this screen.
5 The camera crew were ordered (by the director) to get . . .
6 But because the sun does not rise over the coast of California, they . . .
7 The director told them to get a sunset which they would then run backwards.

120
1 His original ambition was to be an engine driver like his father.
2 The problem is that often you fly over the handlebars.
3 I got the impression that it was trying to get in and we were in danger.
4 I thought you would be interested to hear the outcome of the leopard incident.
5 We did actually manage to find an accordian that we had to mend.
6 We decided to go on to Nepal and get the British Council to sort out the problem.
7 However they were relieved to find a considerate note saying 'Key next door'.
8 It had assured Mrs Kerr that her cooker would be returned pronto.
9 The hero and heroine were to stand on a rocky promontory.
10 I can only conclude that you were very fortunate.

121
In those days a breeding pair could cost as much as £1,800, but prices gradually fell, and since the 1960s chinchillas have become a familiar sight in the home. They are nocturnal, at their most active in the early evening. Greyish-silver – 'standard' – is the most common colour, although light silver, beige, black and white animals are also available.

130
1 selecting, deciding, to include
2 have not visited, are sent, be played, will grow/become/get
3 do, listens, chooses, will play, will suit
4 arrive, given/handed, have been found, planning
5 select, include, can join, being, may/could offend

132
a A list of hotels is attached to this letter
b The enclosed list gives details of courses available this year
c I enclose a cheque for £125 in payment of my course fees
d This bill should be settled by the end of this term
e They settled down quite quickly after all their travelling
f If you're going camping try not to carry too heavy a load
g The lorry had been unevenly loaded, and was therefore very dangerous
h We talked about loads of things
i A valid passport is required for this trip
j You are required to stop and show your passport at the border
k They do not consider a child as important
l Have you considered the position of your family?

136
1 to 2 through 3 from 4 with 5 to 6 in 7 through 8 in 9 of, in 10 of 11 with 12 in

139 a
For, until, in, from, of, on

143 a
a There were five points that Bob Jobbins thought should be remembered.
b It is important to write the information

in an interesting way once it is available.
c It must be easy to understand.
d Unlike the newspaper reader, who can turn back and reread a sentence or two, the radio listener has only one chance.
e One sentence should contain only a limited number of facts.
f The correspondent should begin the report by presenting any vital information necessary to understand the latest development.
g If a correspondent is reporting a plane crash he should not speak in a cheerful voice, which would be sadly out of place.
h In addition, the listener would be confused and distracted.

149
Blast in cinema kills two
£4,000 parking fine
Bouncing baby
British workers pay lower union subscriptions
Junk mail 'welcome'

151
a announced b according c announcement d claimed e reports, rumours f statement g rumours h alleged i believed

154
T: a,c,e,g,i,j,k   F: b,d,f,h

157
a can't find out who to complain to
b companies don't really know who to send their advertising materials to
c how to stop junk mail being sent to them
d would you know who to ask or write to?
e found out what to do
f how to find the time
g knowing which to open and read and which to send back

164
The Government, the Minister of Agriculture, the Government, the farmers, the Government, the farmers, the authorities, the farmers, the Government, the militants, the victims, the ordinary public

173
proposing, option, the whole thing, lucky couple

180 a
a If you had asked me, I would . . .
b Had I known you were coming, I would . . .
c Had you only told me, I could . . .
d Had I thought of it I would . . .
e If he had known what was going to happen, he . . .
f Had the film been a little shorter, we would have enjoyed it much more.

180 b
a marriage b increasingly c equally d equally e friendship f assuming g competition h basic i independence j banned

182 b
1b, 2c

183 a
a . . . rubber boat in which to sleep.
b . . . journey, after which he would meet his girlfriend.
c . . . fishing line with which to catch fish.
d . . . container in which he could collect rainwater.
e . . . Marie-Rose, about whom he thought a lot.
f . . . an interview, in/during which she was asked embarrassing questions.

183 b
pressing, share the cost, richer, drugs, cosmetics, tracts, jungle

187
a attack, attacked b balance, balanced c adopt, adopted, adopt d pour, poured, pouring e sweeping, swept

196 a
was hailed, leaped, had jumped, belongs, wearing, caught, hit, had been leaning, threatening, has left, have lost
b
chatting, climbed, was watching, would have been, jumped, have been

198 a
. . . speak of places they've never been to or people they've never met.
. . . astonishing cases of children who died young apparently being reborn to the same parents.

198 b
. . . of his first two daughters who were

killed in a car crash. They died on the way to church near their home in Hexham, Northumberland.
. . . was told she was pregnant.
. . . that she would have twins, although the doctors said that was unlikely', says John.

202
birthmark, scar, toys, dolls, doll, doll, convinced, experts, evidence

205
a calm b delicate, delicate c calm, rough d delicate e emerged, crept f atmosphere, moderately g rows, deck h emerged

215
a always, even if, actually b hard, hard, soft, soft c making more noise than anyone else

220 b
Suggested sentences:
c In addition to playing with his toy cars, James Thompson from Walsall in the West Midlands also has a real one.
d Although James is only eight years old, he drives a Vauxhall Nova.
e Whenever Steve, his dad, goes for a drive, James climbs into his own car too.
f On seeing how happy the car made James, his dad, who worked at the Irmscher car company continued the production of half-scale cars.
g Steve hoped they could be sold as Christmas presents, despite the fact that they cost £1,800!
h Provided that there were some parents wealthy enough to buy them, the company might manage to make a profit.
i Generally, in the UK you are supposed to be 17 before you are allowed to drive a motor vehicle, but because James does not drive on public roads he does not need a driving licence.

222 a
a Once he had seen how happy James was with his car he decided to make some more/He decided to make some more cars when he saw how happy James was with his.
b Kids may dream about getting a car for Christmas but their parents think only of the £1,800 nightmare tag.
c Considering that each car/in view of the fact that each car takes so long to make, and requires a high standard of workmanship, the price is not actually that bad.

222 b
confusion, consciousness, silence, departure, announcements, tension, space

223 b
development, destroying, report, grow, efficiency, products, campaign

225
a breakages b mileage c shortage d postage e mileage f baggage g leakage

227
Past habit: a d g k Hypothesis: b c h i j l Other (future in the past): e f

234
a As well as being frightened Mr Botibol was excited.
b He could only see one other person.
c It was impossible for Mr Botibol to see her face because her collar . . .
d Mr Botibol was being unusually careful due to the thought of . . .
e He was still not entirely satisfied that this woman . . .
f He simply had to talk to her for a moment beforehand in order to check it.

236
D,A,B

237
1 greatly, soon 2 equally 3 totally, nevertheless 4 increasingly 5 just, awfully 6 obviously, deliberately 7 apparently

240
of: a,b,c,d,e,g,h,j,l to: a (second space), f,i,k

242
1 sit/prob/sol/eval 2 hypoth/eval/conc 3 sit/conc 4 sequence 5 topic/illus 6 topic/illus 7 gen/spec

245
completely, really, highly, absolutely, awfully, merely, quite, terribly, reasonably, unusually, dreadfully, relatively, moderately, entirely, slightly, extremely, surprisingly

63

Grammar Book Key

a, an
1 nineteen, children (10ts x 2)
2 Vannes (10ts)
3 Paris, lived (10ts x 2)

as
1 scouts (20c), involved (20c), Saturday (24)
1.1 number, job (29b ts x 2)
2 possible (24b ts)
2.1 extensive (17b ts end)
3 smile (31)
4 interested (29b ts)
5 career (24)
6 bookings (17b ts), specific (24a ts)

at
1 Print (24b ts)
1.1 14, nobody (102 x 2), matches (14b)
2 nerve (65)
3 dog (59), children (63 ts)
4 travelling (72a), discount (102 part 4)
5 species, case (95 x 2), nothing (100c ts)

be
1 schoolboy (91), formidable (95)
2 others (95), false, species (94 x 2)
3 paragraph (72c), know, Live (91ts)
3.1 Europe (94b ts), horror (95)
4 gulls, potential (80 x 2), brother (87a)
5 eaten, reported, sleeping, Dresden (95 x 4)
6 though (68c ts), muddled (94b ts)

by
1 Office (150a), presenter (163a)
2 warm (38), thing (113)
3 week, February (133a x 2), need (133e)
4 Plaidy (21), Kafue (166b ts)
5 trains (154), births (166c ts)
6 depends (94b ts)

can, could
1 stringer, political (140a ts x 2), always, What (143c x 2)
1.1 month (106a ts)
3 starting, stress (133d x 2)
4 door (109), escaped (116ts)

do
1 telephone (59a), inappropriate (59b)
2 worry, mind, buy (59a ts x 3)
2.1 clothes, handbag, exaggerate (31 x 2)
3 type (25a), window (45b)
4 picture, keep (56a x 2)
5 What (2 ts), required (64)
6 plenty (31), advertise (27 ts)

for
1 one (172b ts), independent (176b)
2.1 levels (176 ts), disqualified (176)
2.2 neighbour (102), basis, feelings (176c ts x 2)
3.1 week, minutes (137 ts x 2), seven (172)

get, got
1 traffic, court (104 x 2), trying, out (110b/c x 2)
2 well (45)
3 stop (72b ts)
4 key, couldn't (110c ts x 2)
5 panicky (110c ts), old, habitation (114 ts x 2)
6 cheaply (95), sort (100c ts)

have
1.1 nice (56a ts)
1.2 sisters (63 ts)
2 handcuffed (72a), gear (72c)
3 tired (64)
4 over (69c ts), driving (69b)
5.1 motorbikes (83 ts), campfire (19)
5.2 lunch (53)
5.3 downstairs (34 ts), dreams (47 ts)
6.1 repertoire (20b), picture (56a ts)
7 missing (38b), handcuffed (72)
8 chin, engine, turned (72b ts x 3)

if
1.1 safe (34), actually (121a ts)
1.2 alterations (45c), might (49 ts)
2 borrow, knew (71 x 2), texts (80c ts)
3 withholding (31), nothing (59)
5 differences (68c ts), how? (72a)

in
1 New York, crawled, window (36 x 3), trapped, Banbury (38 x 2)
1.1 Bristol (24)
2 Scouts (17a ts), audience (27 ts)
3 September (17a ts), moment (34)
4 spelt, draft (24 ts x 2), plenty, business-like (31 x 2)
5 printing (16), full-time (24)
6 fellow (13 ts)

it
1.1 mad, bush, bad, lovely, favourite (4 ts x 5)
1.2 exciting (4) really (17b ts)
2 established (2)
2.1 German (10 ts), accordion (13 ts)
3 hot (4 ts end)

must
1 presentation (143c ts)
2.1 recover (116 ts), newspaper (94b ts)
3 meet (48)
4 France (10 ts)

of
1.1 fraction, broken (87b x 2)
1.2 slice (87a)
1.3 frame (87a), sticky (87b)
2.1 firm, person (25b x 2), 85th (36)
2.2 secret, dreams (47 ts x 2)
3.1 Sort, flow (45 ts x 2), articles (76 ts)
3.2 traditional (21), modern, kinds (43 x 2)
4 man (74)
5 downstairs (34 ts), pram (43 ts)

on
1 sixth, windowsill (150a ts x 2), tanks (184b)
1.2 ground (110b ts) sundeck (210b)
2 Sunday, Saturday (14b x 2), advertised (24)
3 pointers, choice (133e x 2), decision (201)
4 Greece (10 ts), journey (204a ts)
5 stations, radio (130b ts x 2), chat (27 ts)
6.1 Marcos (184)
7 Heathrow (133f)

that
1 genuine, possible, believe (201b ts x 3)
1.1 seventeen (176)
2 strategy (187a), lifted (187b ts)
3.1 workhouse (198a), believe (200)
3.2 subjected (109), hoax (201b ts)
3.3 promise (104), Delhi, representatives (133f x 2)
5 genuine, elements (201c x 2)

the
1.1 86th, safety, floor, specks, artist, idea (36 x 6)
1.2 world (34), Empire (36), sky (43)
1.3 street, list, stairs, light room, chap, door (34 ts x 6)
2 office (43)

to
1 Kathmandu (135), Sherborne (133a)
2 XAL, cheque (135 x 2)
3 grass (124a), speak (137 ts)
4 Birmingham (131 ts), knob (87)
5 communications (131 ts), January (133e)
6 plans (110b ts), normal (114 ts)
7 helpful (133a), likely (133e)
8 sticky, telephone (85 x 2)
9 occasion (20a), area (114 ts)

wh- words
1 beautifully, minds (223a x 2)
2 third (226 ts), still (228b)
3.1 sure, story (217b ts) pool (224a)
3.2 Mr Botibol (228c), could, ever (229b x 2)
4.1 teach (226 ts)
4.2 purser (210a)
5 worst (172b), used (198b)

will
1 embarrassment, action (188a ts x 2)
2 first, say (172b x 2)
3 attack (95), start (114 ts)

with
1 Olympus (200), discussing (215)
2 light, parapet (34 ts x 2), filled, assured (206 x 2)
3 tight, comb (217 x 2), convertible (217b ts)
4 purple (38), twelve (206)
5 continued (207), again (210c ts)

would
1 language (45a), trouble (229b)
2 allowed (210a)
3 cottages, cows (32b x 2), mother (198)
4 dear (53), start (243a ts)
5 like, achieve, rich (232b ts x 3)
6 agree (239a ts), imagine (207b ts)